FACES IN THE FLAMES

A GHOST STORY

Followed by

THE REAL STORY

FACES IN THE FLAMES

A GHOST STORY

Followed by

THE REAL STORY

BY R. FULLEMAN

Faces in the Flames: A Ghost Story
by
R. Fulleman

Cover Design by: David Pascal
Book Design by: Connie Jacobs
Editor: Lorraine Fulleman, MLIS

Distributed by:
    Putnam & Smith Publishing Company
    15915 Ventura Boulevard, Suite 101
    Encino, California 91436
    www.putnamandsmithpublishing.com

Library of Congress Control Number: 2018949651

ISBN: 978-1-939986-23-8

Printed in the United States of America

DEDICATION

I dedicate this book to my late father, Raymond Fulleman. He served aboard two ships during WWII, the U.S.S. *Mobile* (CL-63) and the U.S.S. *Mississinewa* (AO-59). It was his time aboard the *Mississinewa* that prompted me to write this book. My dad has been, and always will be, a hero to me. From his going to sea in the Navy, never expecting to come back alive, to his brave actions when his ship was torpedoed and sinking, to his everyday actions of raising a family, he was the best role model I could have.

ACKNOWLEDGMENTS

I have so many people to thank. First, and foremost, thanks Pop for being there and telling me what happened. Secondly, I have to thank author/historian, Michael Mair who got me into researching the *Miss*. Mike is a wealth of knowledge and a good friend. Thanks to all the *Miss* crewmen I've had the honor to meet and their families who continue to support the memory of the *Miss*. I must also thank Chip and Pam Lambert, and Pat Scannon, who incredibly found the *Miss* under water when no one else could. I'd like to thank the kind people of Ulithi who treat both the ship and its crew with such respect. Thanks to the late Sid Harris and his son, Mike, for their support and the most amazing photos Sid took while ships battled the fires aboard and around the sinking *Miss*. Thanks to the late Margaret Howell (nee Pence) who christened the ship in 1944 for sharing her bond with the *Miss*. I need to thank (then) Commanding Officer, USS *Salvor*, LCDR John A. Carter, USN who oversaw the removal of the oil from the sunken *Miss*, as well as the construction of a memorial at Ulithi. Plus, I need to thank my twin brother, Bob Fulleman, who has also put great effort into getting the story of the *Miss* out to the public. Lastly, and by no means least, I must thank my most ardent supporter, my beautiful wife, Lorraine, who has put up with me and helped me every step of the way.

PREFACE

This book contains two stories: one a ghost story based on historical fiction. It tells the story of a young boy whose love and admiration of his grandpa lead him through an adventure which ends in solving a half century old mystery.

The other story is a true, non-fictionalized account of the sinking of the USS *Mississinewa* and the first use of a suicide submarine by the Imperial Japanese Navy in WWII. The story covers the real experiences of about a dozen men, officers and crew, and their escape from the flames.

They were incredibly brave.

(Words with an * can be found in the Glossary on page 203.)

BOOK
ONE

CHAPTER ONE

November 1944 – the Attack

"What the …?" Cameron Lund said as he fell. Before he could finish, he landed on the gray steel deck of the ship. It happened so fast he didn't have time stop his fall. He had been sleeping in his bunk. His fall had woken him up. *Who was the wise guy*, he wondered? Looking around, he saw others shipmates on the deck too.

Lund scrambled to his feet. "What gives?" he yelled to nearby sailors.

"I think the ship's been hit," was the first reply. "Maybe an accident up forward," one guy said.

"Maybe . . .," but that thought was cut off. A second huge blast went off. The whole ship lifted up and then dropped down. At the same time, it rocked left and right. The power to move the 23,000 ton ship like that scared Lund. He grabbed the edge of his bunk to steady himself. Through an open hatch Lund could see the sky filled with flames. He looked at the hatch that led to the fire room. The fire room was where he worked aboard the ship. The boilers that powered the ship were there.

Lund turned to his friend, Bowers, who was just getting up. "Bowers . . . gotta get to our battle stations. This is big!"

Bowers started forward to the engine room hatch.

Lund only saw the back of his friend as Lund jumped through the fire room doorway. That was the last time he ever saw Bowers.

Outside, hot oil rained down on everyone there. The sounds of the blasts echoed off the steel walls of the fire room.

Sailors were already in the fire room when Lund got there. Reed and Duffy were at their work stations. Lund went straight to his work station. He controlled the water going to the boilers. Too much water would flood a boiler. Too little water and the boiler would overheat and break down.

The fire room chief, Smitty, got there just after Lund. Smitty started directing the men. As they worked, more blasts outside increased their worries. Smitty sent Duffy topside to see what was going on with the ship. Almost right away, the blasts increased. The men were there for about 15 minutes. Lund prayed all the more with each explosion he heard.

As Lund worked near the hatch, the ship's captain stopped just outside. The captain yelled in to Lund, "Get off the ship. It's going down."

Lund didn't have to be told twice. It had been the longest 15-minutes of his life, so far. He yelled over to the men at the boilers, "The Captain said to let it go. She's going down!" So, the men quickly shut down all the boilers, except one. That one would supply some power to the ship if needed.

"Quick, out the starboard hatch!" Smitty ordered. But, when they opened the hatch on the right side of the ship, thick black smoke poured in. The men could barely breath. They slammed the hatch shut. Then, the men ran over to the port side hatch. This left side hatch looked better. Only a small amount of smoke hovered in the hallway.

With the crazy things going on, the Chief forgot Duffy. The three men started towards the back of the ship. Suddenly, he remembered. "Wait, where's Duffy?" Smitty asked the men. Smitty wasn't sure if Duffy ever came back to the fire room. "Lund, go back and make sure Duffy got out of the fire room." Smitty and Reed started aft.

Lund stuck his head in the fire room hatch and yelled for Duffy. Lund didn't know Duffy was told to go topside. Lund could only see thick black smoke in the fire room from the hatchway. Lund knew it was no use. Duffy couldn't still be alive if he was down in the fire room.

That thick smoke now made it hard to see in the hallway. From somewhere, Lund heard a guy yell, "You can't go back aft. Fire is setting off the ammo there!"

Lund turned and said to himself, "Dear God, my mom's going to get word I'm dead." Just as he said this, a man ran through the smoke at the end of the hallway. Lund just barely saw him. *If that guy can make it out that way, maybe I can too.* So, Lund ran through the smoke, following the other man. He found his way to the lowest deck on the ship. He could see flames around the entire ship. Some of those flames were at least 200 feet high. There was just one slim wedge of water free of flames. He lowered himself over the side and swam out. Just beyond the edge of the flames were boats from nearby ships. One of the boats pulled Lund aboard.

From the small rescue boat, Lund could see men still on the sinking ship. Some men jumped into the burning water. He could see some trying to swim under the flames. He said a prayer for them as he helped pull men into the small boat. Still, some died there in the boat. He thought of the men dying inside the ship . . . alone. Their families would never know how they died.

Later that day, all the survivors got to a nearby ship. Lund found Reed. They looked for Chief Smitty and

Duffy, but no one had seen them. They and his friend Bowers were never found. It was the saddest day of young Cameron Lund's life.

On the ship, officers told the men more of what happened. It was then that Lund heard 63 men had died. It was an enemy suicide sub that hit them.

CHAPTER TWO

Adventure and Danger Comes Again

Many Years Later

Why'd they have to sink that ship way out here? Cam asked in his head. *If the Germans had sunk it, we'd be there by now.* Cam looked down and shook his head left and right. He knew he was just being silly. He was just so tired of traveling. His drooping head and slumped shoulders showed it.

"Sorry, son. We've still got at least a couple more hours. Then we have to change to the next plane," Cam's dad said. He was just as tired of traveling as Cam. The seats in the plane lost their comfort a long time ago. He shifted in his seat. He had lost track himself as to how much longer they still had to go.

He looked over at his 15-year-old son, Cam. Bill Lund was proud of his son, Cam. He named Cam after his dad. He knew the trip was tough on Cam. He also knew it would be the trip of a lifetime.

Cam had loved his grandpa. He was Cam's hero. The old sailor had lots of stories. Cam would sit and listen to his grandpa talk about the past. His war stories sounded scary. He promised his grandpa that someday he would dive on his ship. He would see what his grandpa went through in the war.

Cam was average size for his age. His hair was a very

light brown and he had blue eyes. He looked a lot like his grandpa did when he was that age.

"Things will be great when we get there," he told Cam. At least, that's what he hoped. Cam's dad always tried to look on the bright side of things. Arranging the trip had been a lot of work for Cam's dad. He had to get the okay from the chief at Ulithi. He had to explain why they wanted to dive on the shipwreck. The chief said yes, but the father and son would need to dive with local guides. The guides would meet the two when they got to Ulithi.

Ulithi is an atoll. An atoll is a group of tiny islands. A volcano makes the islands. The volcano forms a peak. The mountain peak grows up and out of the ocean. The peak is open in the middle, kind of like a donut. The peak forms a circle of small islands in the water. All this makes up an atoll. Ulithi Atoll is in the Pacific Ocean.

Cam had heard the travel plans, but now they seem so different. At first, it all sounded thrilling. He could barely believe it. His dad signed them up for SCUBA* diving lessons. His dad wanted them to SCUBA dive on a sunken ship. "Diving down so deep is risky. Of course, all SCUBA diving can be risky. That's why we must take lessons. We need to learn how to dive safely," Cam's dad had said to Cam. "But, diving is the only way to see the ship."

The sunken ship was the one Cam's grandpa served on. He was in the Navy during WWII*. Now, the ship sits in 130 feet of water. In WWII, a submarine sank the ship. In this case, they changed a torpedo into a sub. A man could steer the sub. The idea was to lose one man in order to sink a ship.

Cam had heard many stories from his grandpa about the ship. So, Cam knew there would be adventure. There had to be! Plus, maybe a little bit of danger. He figured he was ready for some danger, too.

He never thought he'd get bored on the trip. But now

boredom washed over him in waves. The length of the trip seemed to grow with each passing second. He had doubts he would ever get to the adventure part. He was sure there couldn't be any danger left at this point. *Well, maybe the danger of dying from boredom*, he thought.

The trip was long. They had flown six hours to get to Los Angeles from Maryland. After that, they flew for 15 more hours. They took 3 planes before they, at last, got to the island of Yap. Each plane seemed to be smaller and smaller than the one before. The thrill of the trip faded as time stretched on. It felt like they were traveling to the end of the earth.

When Cam and his dad got to Yap Island, things changed for them. They felt like they were entering a different world. All the plants and trees were extra green and there were lots of them. The view looked like a scene from out of one of Cam's video games. As they got off the plane, the thick, damp air was like a wall of water. *That's why things grow so well here*, thought Cam. *The air is so damp. You never feel that in a video game. I guess no one would buy one if they did.* He gave a short chuckle to his own joke.

His wet clothes and skin took his mind off his joke right away. Cam felt awful. He went into the airport building as fast as he could. He hoped the air would be dryer inside.

Cam was out of luck. The small building had no air-conditioning. The air inside was just a little dryer. Cam sat down and watched their bags.

Many people sat in the small terminal. Cam noticed a pretty, young girl in the crowd. She had rich dark skin and long brown hair. He hoped to meet some kids his age. *Of course, meeting pretty girls like her would be even better*, he thought.

Cam looked around for his dad. He saw him not far

away near a big sign. The sign read *Pacific Missionary Airlines*. Under the sign was a simple looking desk. Behind the desk stood a man in a short-sleeved white shirt, and black slacks. Next to him was a woman in a while top and black shorts. She had an airline badge on her top. Cam's dad talked to the man and then shook his hand. Then, the man pointed to a small doorway.

Cam's dad walked back to Cam with a smile on his face. He said, "Come on. We can go get on the plane now." Cam was a bit surprised. They didn't have to wait for an announcement to board the plane. Cam picked up his bags, relieved this would be the last leg of the trip. His dad picked up the other bags and led the way to the door.

Cam wondered, *shouldn't we have checked these bags in*? *Doesn't the airline have to load them on the plane*? He thought it odd, but his dad didn't say anything. Cam followed dragging his bags.

They walked back out into the hot, damp air. Cam saw the man who had been at the desk. He was taking the bags from Cam's dad. He carried them twenty feet and then set them down. Cam looked around. He expected to see a jet plane, but none were there. Parked in front of them was a very small, 8-passenger plane. The plane was nice and clean but was very small. It really didn't look like it could hold a lot of dive gear. The plane barely looked able to hold the three of them. Cam had never been on such a small plane before.

"Are we going to fit on that plane?" Cam asked his dad. "Is there room for us?" He worried there might be some big guy in the seat next to him. It had happened on an earlier flight.

"I'm not so sure, Cam," his dad said. Then, he gave a slight chuckle and shake of his head. "But, I promise you, this is the last plane we need to take to get there." Cam's dad was tired of the traveling too. He welcomed the last leg of the trip. "But, remember, this is where the adventure begins."

Faces in the Flames: A Ghost Story

CHAPTER THREE

Where the Adventure Begins

"Hi, I'm Captain Peters. I'll be flying you to Ulithi today. As soon as we get all your gear stowed on board the plane, we'll be taking off." Luckily, all the gear did fit onto the plane. The bags with their clothes were not too big. The tricky parts were the big bags with SCUBA diving gear. With some extra pushing, all the gear fit onto the plane.

Cam didn't have a say as to where he sat in the plane. He got the seat right behind the pilot's seat. His dad got to sit in the seat next to the pilot. Cam was okay with his dad sitting next to the pilot. He knew his dad could chat with the adult better than he could. Also, Cam was very tired. He thought he would probably fall asleep on the trip.

Cam kept looking out the small window of the plane. At first, the small space inside the cabin felt tight. Cam's head almost touched the ceiling. He could probably touch both walls at the same time, too. He felt uneasy. He had gotten used to being in bigger airplanes. He hoped the small space wouldn't bother him once they got up into the air.

Cam mostly just stared out of his window. He had long since run out of battery for his phone. Fortunately, the day was bright and clear. Big, fluffy clouds dotted the sky. To Cam, they looked like white cotton candy. There was nothing but blue shades of sea below. Now and then, small, white waves broke on the water.

From the height of the airplane, the water looked quite calm. Cam asked how high they were flying. The pilot checked his gauges. He pointed to a gauge on the instrument panel. The gauge showed 2,000 feet. Cam wished there would be some solid ground to see below. He didn't like it. After that, he kept busy looking at two gauges; the one that showed height and the fuel gauge. For the rest of the flight, his head filled with thoughts of a crash landing at sea. He hoped they were almost there. *How much farther is it?* he said, this time just to himself.

CHAPTER FOUR

Where in the Pacific Ocean is Ulithi Atoll?

They had flown for just less than an hour when the pilot pointed to the sea. "There is Ulithi Atoll." He had to shout a bit to his passengers so they could hear him. "Just a group of small islands formed by an old volcano. Most of the land is just 5 feet above sea level." *Great! Now I can worry about that*, thought Cam. He never thought about how low the islands were. This trip was not like what Cam first expected.

Only small dots were visible in the ocean. Cam's dad could barely make them out. Cam could see them only when he sat up. He wasn't sure if they were big enough to land on.

As they neared, things changed. The dots changed into small white blotches*. As they neared, bright green dots seemed to grow larger in the white areas.

When they got real close, Cam could see the white was waves. The waves were breaking onto the reefs of the islands. Reefs were around all the islands. The water looked white from the bubbles made by the splashing waves.

The small plane circled around the islands. As it did, the pilot said, "I'll point out a few things for you to see." The plane leaned to the left and went in a big circle. "The long, blue building there on the left is the high school. The tall building there is the Catholic church. We're coming up to the island of Sorlan. Over there is our landing strip."

Cam's dad looked concerned. "That sure doesn't look like much to land on," he told the pilot. "I guess it's long enough, though, huh?"

"Don't worry. The landing strip is long enough," the pilot said. Cam's dad still didn't like the short runway.

A brief metallic hum filled the cabin. A click followed the hum. That meant the plane's wheels came down and locked into place. A loud screech and a puff of smoke came from the tires as they hit the runway. The sound surprised Cam. He jumped a little bit. A blur of green palm trees sped past the windows of the plane.

Cam's dad looked impressed with the landing. "That was a great landing," Cam's dad told the pilot.

The pilot nodded, "Thanks. I get a lot of practice. I fly this same trip each Saturday. After all of you get off the plane, I load mail and go right back," the pilot said. Like always, Captain Peters didn't wait long to get back on his way to Yap.

Nearby, stood a big man with a wide smile. He walked up to Cam and his dad. Seeing him, they felt a little out of place. They both had light skin color. They had lots of luggage. Cam's dad wore a button up shirt with a collar. They both felt like quite the city folks.

The man wore a large cloth that looked kind of like a towel around his waist. A string of native flowers was around his neck. On his feet, he wore flip-flops. A wide nose, brown eyes, and a broad smile made up his face. Bits of gray in his hair did not match his skin, darkened by a life in the sun.

"Hello! You must be Mr. Lund and his son, Cam," the man said, keeping his big smile. "I'm Kai. Welcome to Ulithi Atoll." He reached out to shake hands. His hand was strong, being used to a lot of work.

Mr. Lund and Cam reached out and shook hands with Kai.

"Let me help you with your dive gear. We'll load it into this truck. After that, we can get you to the hotel. I'm sure you must be tired. The trip from the mainland takes a lot out of you," Kai said. "I went there once. I still remember how tired I felt."

"Great," Mr. Lund replied. "The trip has been *very* long." Kai's concern for them impressed him.

A small group of boys crowded around to hear what was going on. Before Cam and his dad could reach for their bags, the boys picked up the bags. They wanted to help. Soon, the bags and diving gear were all in the small truck. The three of them squeezed into the cab of the truck.

The ride was very short. In just 5 minutes they reached the edge of the beach. At the water's edge was a 20-foot long, open boat. The boys did not stay around after they put the bags down. The boys seemed a little shy. They hid their faces when Cam looked at them but looked back right away.

Cam felt guests did not come to Ulithi often. Everyone they passed by stopped to watch. Most of the people stared as they went by. *Was this how everyone would treat me and my dad?* he thought.

CHAPTER FIVE

Welcome to the Tropics

"Here's where we take you to Falalop. That's where the hotel is," Kai said. "A short boat ride will get us there. Since the water is calm, the ride should be nice."

"As you can see, there is no dock. We will have to walk out to the boat," Kai said.

Cam and his dad took off their shoes. Then, with shoes and socks in hand, they waded through the water to the boat. The water came just above their knees. The warmth of the water surprised them. Where they lived, the water was always cold. Here in the tropics, the water was just right. Not too cold, nor too hot. The sand beneath their feet had a lot of seashells. It made the walk to the boat exciting, but hard. They had to be careful not to step on the sharp shells. Cam was careful where he stepped. The last thing he wanted was to fall into the water. The good thing was the water was clear. He could see where not to step.

Kai put all the gear on the boat. Cam and his dad got in next. Lifting the front of the boat, Kai gave it a small push. He then hopped into the boat. He started the old motor and it sputtered to life. They were off.

Kai was right about the ride being nice. The whole trip to the island of Falalop was smooth. Only some low swells* rocked the boat. The time went by quickly. Kai used the time to tell Cam and his dad about the islands. Cam could not pay attention to the story well. He tried but couldn't.

Try as he might, he could not keep his eyes open. The long trip, warm sun, and mild sway of the boat lulled him to sleep right away.

The small boat finally came to rest on a quiet beach. Cam felt his father giving his shoulder a shake to wake him.

"Get up son, we're here." It took Cam a minute or two to clear the sleep from his head. He felt a little groggy. The nap was too short to have helped him. He was too tired to wake up completely.

Two teenagers came to greet the boat. One was a well-tanned, good looking boy. He looked very strong. The other was a pretty girl with an eye-catching body. The wind blew the girl's long, curly, black hair into her face. The boy had similar hair but shorter. Cam guessed the boy and girl were around his age. He couldn't tell exactly. The boy and girl stared at Cam's eyes. They stopped only when their father asked, "Are you two going to help?" Their faces got a little red and they looked down.

"Oh, sorry," the young boy said. It was unusual for them to see such blue eyes. The local people all had brown eyes.

"This is Tony and Vera, my kids. This is Mr. Lund and his son, Cam," Kai said. "Let's get them to the hotel so they can rest up from their long trip."

The two island teens didn't say anything more. They picked up the bags with ease and carried them to the hotel.

The boy, Tony, dressed just like his dad. The girl, Vera, dressed a lot like her brother. But, she had a t-shirt on as well as the cloth around her waist. All of them wore rubber sandals on their feet. The cloth is called a lava lava. A lot of the islanders wear them.

Cam had not seen many islanders up to that point in time. He wondered if they all looked like Tony and Vera. Both Tony and Vera had very smooth skin. Their eyes were brown and friendly. The two had constant* smiles on their faces. Right away he knew he would like his time on the islands. *I wonder if Vera has a boyfriend.*

Faces in the Flames: A Ghost Story

CHAPTER SIX

The Hotel

This island had no dock, too. In fact, there were no docks on any of the islands there. Wading ashore had helped to fully awaken Cam. He was glad the water wasn't cold. He didn't want to wake up too fast.

Once out of the water, the walk was short. He noticed how white the sand was. Back home the sand was brown. He'd have to ask about that later. Right now, he was too tired to care much. He wanted to make sure he wouldn't step on anything sharp. There were many seashells on the sand.

At last, Cam got a chance to look up at the hotel. It looked just like in the photos on the internet. The hotel had two levels with five rooms on each level. Six of the rooms faced the water. The other four had views of a lush*, green garden. The building had a flat roof and wooden siding. Fresh paint gave the hotel a clean look. There were stairs going up outside the building to the second floor. The room Cam and his dad shared was upstairs facing the water.

Cam was relieved to get to the hotel. The flights had taken over 24 hours to get there. Check-in took a few minutes so Cam found a chair to sit down in. Things on the island seemed to move more slowly than they did back home. Both dad and son were happy when they got help taking their bags to their room.

Their first thoughts of the room were that it was simple. The room had two single beds, a small table, and a chair. The artwork on the walls looked like it was made on the island. Then, they saw the room looked very clean and restful. They liked that. They knew costs were high to bring things to the islands.

Even being a simple room, it was nice. The two felt better right away in their room. Windows on both sides of the room were open a little bit. A slight breeze blew through the room. It made the room just perfect. Cam started to feel better the moment he felt the breeze.

Cam was a little down when he saw they had no Wi-Fi in the room. He figured there would be Wi-Fi downstairs. He was just glad to be able to plug in his phone to charge. He went right to his bed. The bed was quite a welcome sight.

The long hours in the planes and cool island breeze took their toll. Right after Cam and his dad put their things down, they both fell onto their beds. The last thing Cam heard was his dad say, "I love an ocean breeze." They fell asleep right away.

At 4 o'clock, Cam's dad gently shook Cam awake. "We'd better get up. We need to see what's here before it gets dark," Mr. Lund said.

Cam had a hard time waking up. His dad kept asking him, "You getting up?" About 3 times of that was enough. "Ok, ok, I'm up!" Cam knew he would be better off to just get up.

Kai surprised them in the hotel lobby. He was sitting there, waiting for them.

"Glad to see you've been able to get some rest." He could tell they must have taken a nap. Both visitors looked a lot more refreshed.

"We needed it. I do feel a lot better now," Mr. Lund replied. "I hope you weren't sitting here waiting for us all this time?"

"No, not long. I knew you would take a nap. We had friends to visit nearby. Tony and Vera are still there. Since you've rested, I'll show you around a little. Then, you can have dinner. We will want to get an early start in the morning. The trip to the dive site takes a while. We expect to have good weather each day this week. If the weather is not good, we cannot dive down to the ship. The water will be too rough."

The ship! Cam thought. The ship was the USS *Mississinewa*. Most everyone now calls it the "*Miss*" since the full name is so hard to say. Cam's grandpa served on board the *Miss* in the Navy. That was back in World War II. He was on the ship when it sank. The ship broke into two pieces. It is lying on the bottom of the ocean.

A suicide submarine had hit the ship. The submarine was made from a torpedo. The submarine blew up when it hit his ship. The Japanese Navy used these subs. They were desperate* to not lose the war. Cam's grandpa was lucky to get off the ship before it sank. Sixty-three men had died when the ship sank. The ship sank in the year 1944.

Cam is 15 years old now. He was ten when his grandpa died after living a long life. He can still recall the stories his grandpa told him though. Cam has always been proud of his grandpa. He was proud his grandpa fought in the war. He misses not being able to talk to him. "This will be so cool tomorrow," Cam said to his dad. His happy smile became a little sad. "I only wish Grandpa was still with us to talk about it."

That night Cam had a hard time falling asleep. *Maybe the nap or the new bed is to blame*, Cam tried to tell himself. Cam tossed and turned. He couldn't stop thinking. *Were those few deep-water dives enough,* he thought? He started to doubt himself. He was pretty new to diving. At last, he fell into a deep sleep.

CHAPTER SEVEN

Diving on the USS *Mississinewa*

The next morning brought a change in Cam. The light of day and some deep sleep had filled him with new confidence. He was ready for the dive. Cam didn't know it yet, but he was a little too confident.

When Cam and his dad came down, there sat Kai and his kids. They were waiting in the lobby. Tony and Kai were in t-shirts and swimsuits. Vera wore an island wrap over her swim suit. Cam and his dad were in their swimsuits, eager to dive on the *Miss*. "We knew you wanted to get an early start today," Kai said. Like Cam and his dad, they too were eager to dive down to the ship.

The five of them carried the dive gear to the boat. The heavy gear was a bit of a struggle. Walking through the sand was hard. *It sure would have been easier with a dock*, Cam thought. *Glad we're getting help from Vera and Tony.*

Their bulky gear just fit into the boat. They had to be careful how they loaded the boat. The others' gear was already in the boat. With enough pushing and pulling, all the gear went into place.

Cam was glad to see Tony get into the boat. He was even more glad to see Vera get in. He wasn't sure they would be coming with them. Before Cam knew it, they were on their way to the wreck.

"It'll take about an hour to get out to the wreck," Kai said. "Vera, Tony, and I will be diving with you. Be sure to be careful. Going so deep and around a ship is dangerous. We want to make sure we are with you each dive you make."

Cam lost track of the time. At last, the sound of the engine on the small boat became quieter. Cam could tell the boat was coming to a stop, but where? They seemed to be in the middle of the ocean. Cam could barely see any of the islands.

Kai slowly steered the boat up to a large red ball floating on the water. Cam couldn't think how the red ball came to be in the middle of nowhere. He thought maybe Kai would get the ball into the boat. The ball was really a buoy to tell ships where the *Miss* was. The buoy has a rope tied to it. The other end of the rope tied to the back end of the *Miss*. The buoy stays there all the time. The buoy makes knowing where the *Miss* is on the ocean floor easier.

Cam became very eager to get into the water. It seemed to take a long time for everyone to put on their gear. They checked and double-checked the valves and air tanks. Getting into a wetsuit on a small boat is hard to do. Each tug on the neoprene* suits caused the boat to rock back and forth. All that rocking of the boat started to upset Cam's stomach. He was feeling queasy*. He hoped they could get in the water soon.

Cam and his dad had to buy warm water wetsuits for this trip. The water near their home was cold most of the year. Here the water was much warmer. Both Cam and his dad were amazed* Kai did not use a wetsuit at all. The water would be cooler the deeper they dove. Kai was going to dive in just a swimsuit and t-shirt. Both Vera and Tony had on thin wetsuits. At last, all suited up and were ready to go down. Cam didn't think about it at the time, but this is when the danger began.

CHAPTER EIGHT

For Your Safety, Please Stay Together

Kai made it clear he was in charge of the dives. Kai paired up the divers. Cam's dad would swim with Tony, and Cam would swim with Vera. That way, Kai could keep an eye on everyone. He was the most experienced with the wreck.

"Do not forget, stay together down there," Kai said. "I don't want anyone going off on their own. It is too dangerous and we only have so much air in our tanks. Stay with your diving buddy."

"You know what they taught us in diving class," Cam's dad said to his son. "This ship has been down there for over 70 years. There can be a lot of dangerous things there."

"That's right. The ocean storms move things on the ocean floor. And, there are some fishing nets caught on the wreck," Kai said. "They are very hard to see in the water. The fishing lines are hard to see. Also, most of the ship is upside down. If you move things, they can fall down very easily. And remember, most of the metal is sharp!"

Kai told them all what to expect when they got down to the ship. He also told them how they should go around the ship. They would start at the back of the ship and swim forward. Lastly, he showed them hand signals. They need to use them in the water since they could not talk to each other.

"Remember one more thing," Kai said. "The ship is a gravesite. At least 20 of the 63 men died in the ship. We cannot go inside."

Cam had to stop and think about that. He never thought about men left in the ship. He thought they took all the dead sailors and buried them. He recalled stories of men who died getting off the ship. Some of the men were friends of his grandpa. Tears were in his grandpa's eyes when he talked about his pals. *That's why he didn't talk about them much*, Cam thought. It made Cam sad. He didn't see his grandpa cry any other time. The idea of being by graves made him worry a little.

Vera was first to dive in and Cam went next. He didn't want Vera to think he feared anything. Cam and Vera swam away from the boat. They were just a few feet under when they heard splashing sounds. His dad and Tony swam to him. Lastly, Cam heard the splash and saw Kai in the water.

Because of what Kai had said, Cam did not think the water would be clear. He and his dad had only dived in the Atlantic Ocean. There, they could only see about 20 feet or so. Today, Cam couldn't trust his eyes. He could see for at least 75 feet. The clarity of the water made him want to get down to the ship all that much more.

Vera and Tony held onto the buoy's rope. They waited for everyone to come near. Then, the pairs started swimming down. Kai motioned for everyone to use the rope as a guide. He pulled himself along the rope to show how it should be done.

Going down seemed to take a long time. Cam was glad he was wearing gloves. The rope had some seaweed growing on it. When he wasn't watching where he grabbed the rope, Cam watched Vera. Cam watched the bubbles come out of Vera's mouthpiece. He watched the bubbles as they got bigger and floated up, out of sight. Watching the bubbles was a thing that always charmed him.

Cam was glad to be paired with Vera. He thought she was very pretty. He didn't have a girlfriend back home but would like to. He was eager to tell his friends about this pretty girl. He made sure his dad took a picture of the two together. His mind started to wander. He thought about Vera with a cramp* in the water. He could rescue her and be her hero. He imagined her giving him a big kiss. That would make quite a picture for his friends to see. For sure, he would have to post that online.

Cam woke from his daydream when he caught a glimpse of the *Miss*. Indeed, he wasn't 100% sure what he saw was the *Miss*. He saw a huge thing resting on the sandy ocean floor. Around the shape, he saw a flow of color. The hulking shape seemed to be alive. He quickly brought his focus back to see what was there. The flow was thousands of fish swimming around the ship. Cam had never seen so many fish before. The colors on the fish were bright, happy colors. It looked like a living wall of color. The fish darted one way and then another. Then, the distinct gray color of the ship stood out. Cam saw the real shape of the ship last. The color of the fish stood in stark contrast to the gray ship.

Faces in the Flames: A Ghost Story

CHAPTER NINE

At Last, the *MISS*

From what Cam could make out, the ship was upside down. First, he saw the propellers. Then, he saw the rudder. The propellers each had four big blades. Propellers, or props, push the ships along. They were 16 feet across, from blade tip to blade tip. The props had what looked like plants attached to them. They were long and swaying in the current. As he looked, a memory came to Cam. He recalled seeing a photo of the ship. The ship had turned upside down before sinking. The back end of the ship stuck up into the air. The back end of the ship still looked the same now. All the parts of the ship were in the same place as in the photo.

Cam felt a tap on his shoulder. He turned to look back and he saw his dad. His dad was giving him two "thumbs up." His dad was telling Cam, 'Look, we got to your grandpa's ship.'

Cam beamed with pride, too. He could see his dad's smiling face through the diving mask.

Cam and Vera started to swim along the ship. Cam sped up, but Vera caught the tip of his fin. He forgot to wait and swim next to Vera. Cam saw her give him a signal to stay together. Cam was super excited to see the ship. Vera had seen the ship before. She wasn't as excited as Cam. She knew her dad was counting on her to keep

Cam as safe as she could.

They spent 20 minutes going around the back end of the ship. Cam's dad had a camera that was waterproof. He took a ton of photos. Cam and his dad even took a selfie. At one point, Cam took off his glove so he could touch the ship with his bare hand. When he touched it, he thought he felt a small shock. The shock felt like getting zapped touching a doorknob. He wasn't sure what to think of it. His focus promptly went back to viewing the ship.

An urge* came over Cam to see the entire ship, all at once. He didn't think how big the ship was. He forgot the ship was almost the length of two football fields. In his eagerness, Cam turned to swim to the front of the ship. Kai knew how Cam felt but motioned they needed to go up. Vera saw her dad and grabbed Cam to stop him.

Time had gone by much faster than Cam or his dad realized. It was good Kai was watching the gauges on his air tank. He knew it was time to end this dive. The divers swam back to the buoy rope before going up. They used the rope to ease their way up. They could rise no faster than their slowest bubbles. That was the safest way to go up. Before long they came to a waiting depth of fifteen feet. They had to stay there for 15 minutes. After that, they could go the rest of the way. Waiting was important while going up from so great a depth. Going up too fast could make the diver ill or even die.

Cam and his dad found the whole dive thrilling. As soon as they could, they started talking. Their delight was catching. Big smiles came on Vera and Tony's faces. Even Kai could feel the emotions in the air.

"Your Grandpa talked about that ship for so many years, Cam. It's hard to think we're really seeing it," Cam's dad said. Cam's dad shook his head back and forth in disbelief as he spoke.

"I can't wait to go back down and see more," Cam

said. "I sure wish Grandpa was here to see this."

"Well, Cam, it's probably best he wasn't here. He told me that day was the saddest day in his life, watching his ship sink."

"Don't worry," Kai said, "we will come back tomorrow. Keep in mind, you can only be down that deep for a short time each day. Too much time that deep is dangerous."

Cam thought, *I wonder what we'll see tomorrow.*

CHAPTER TEN

A Warning from a Strange Source

Cam and his dad came down to eat early the next day. There, they found Kai, Vera, and Tony waiting. Kai's little girl, Lea, waited there too. Lea was a very cute 5-year old girl. She wore a t-shirt that fit her more like a dress. The t-shirt had a large print of a tropical flower. The shirt came down nearly to her ankles. Her long dark curly hair looked a lot like Vera's.

Lea was shy and clung to her daddy's leg when Cam and his dad got there.

"I'm sorry. Lea has been like this all morning. We will have to wait for a couple of minutes for my wife to get here. Lea didn't want me to go out to the ship this morning," Kai said.

Lea peeked around her daddy's leg and said, "No, Daddy." You can go, but the strangers should not! They're going to take something," she said. "You said no one should ever take anything from the big ship."

"No, dear. Everything will be fine. They know not to take anything from the ship." Kai looked at Cam and his Dad as he said that. His eyebrows came up as if to ask the two if he was right. "I'll watch out for the ship."

"No, Daddy! It's not the ship, it's the men who live on it. They will be mad."

"Lea, you know nobody lives on the ship. How could they? The ship is deep under water." Just then, his wife appeared in the doorway. "Look, Mama is here now," Kai said rather relieved. "Mama will take you back home. I will make sure nothing bad happens today," he said. "I will make sure. Don't you worry." He soon forgot about Lea thinking men still lived on the ship.

The little girl kept shaking her head. Her mother picked her up and started to walk out the door. Her dad gave her a reassuring look and nod. "I will see you when I get back."

"I'm sorry about that. She's just 5 and gets some strange ideas in her head at times," Kai said.

Cam became concerned when he got to the boat. The water was not as calm as the day before. The swells in the atoll were bigger. There were more clouds today, too.

A look of concern came on Mr. Lund's face. He asked, "Are we going to be able to dive on the ship today? The weather doesn't look so good."

"Sure, it's just we are going out earlier today. The clouds will burn off later."

Most of the boat ride to the buoy was quieter than yesterday. Everyone was deep in thought about what the day might bring. The only sound came from the boat's old motor. The boat bounced up and down in the heavier swells in the water. Everyone in the boat had to hold on to the side of the boat.

Before they got to the dive spot, Kai said, "Now, just to remind you. You must not take anything from the ship. Chief Pisante said no one is to take anything from the site. The ship is a burial ground for the sailors who died here."

"I would like to take a keepsake*, but I understand. Our keepsakes will just have to be our photos," Cam's dad said. He held up his camera to show he agreed.

"That's a good way to look at it," Tony said.

Cam understood too, but he was a bit sad. He knew the basic story of the sinking. Since they got there, he learned more about the ship. There were 63 men who died when the ship sunk. Close to 40 of those men died from the blast. They never left the ship. *Will the guys back home believe all my stories*, he wondered? Some of his friends have relatives who had been in the army. They had lots of stories to tell. They also had keepsakes to show. Cam had no way of knowing then how much he would be bringing home.

Faces in the Flames: A Ghost Story

CHAPTER ELEVEN

Some Things are a Lot Sharper Than They Look

Kai was right. By the time they reached the dive spot, the sun had come out. The swells died down a bit too. Kai had Tony tie the small boat up to the floating red buoy. "Just so you know, there are two buoys on the ship," Kai told the others. "This buoy has *Bow* written on it. A bow is the front of a ship. Today we will dive on the front of the ship. Going down from here will save us a lot of dive time getting to the bow."

Cam and his dad were excited. They were hoping to see more of the ship. Today they would. Yesterday, they could only dive on the back end of the ship. Since the back of the ship is upside down, there is not so much to see there. The decks of the ship are in the sand on the ocean floor. The front part of the ship is lying on its left side deep into the sand.

The group was halfway to the ship before they could make out its shape. They were glad they had the rope to guide them straight to the ship. The closer they got, the more damage they could see. The front part of the ship had the most damage. The blast from the sub had blown a large hole in the side of the ship. After that blast, gasoline fumes on the ship had blown up. The second blast tore the ship in two. That's why the back part of the ship is upside down.

Up closer, the divers could see the front part of the ship well. The links of the anchor chain draped off the side of the ship. The other end of the chain lay buried under the sand.

A large gun mount sat on the front section of the ship. Seaweed and coral covered the barrel of the gun. The coral made the shape of the gun hard to make out. Cam thought about his grandpa having been on the ship. He could almost see him standing by the gun during the war. *I'll bet he was super brave*, Cam thought. *I'll bet there was a lot of noise and guys running around.* The gun looked very quiet and peaceful now. Just the fish swimming around the area.

The other part of the ship had a look of fury. The metal edges of the ship were all twisted. The shapes gave a feeling of rage. Some of the old metal shards had seaweed growing on them. When the plants moved in the current*, the ship looked scarier. The cloudy skies above let less light down to the ship. There were a lot more shadows on the ship today.

Cam used his air supply much better today. He tried to be calmer. He didn't breathe so hard. He didn't try to see everything at once. The day before, he was just too eager and used up his air too fast.

While he was looking at a small part of the ship, Vera touched his arm. Cam looked up at Vera. She pointed to Cam's dad. He waved his hand at Cam and Vera. He held up his camera and pointed at them. Cam took a second to understand. *Oh, a photo of him and Vera. That would be cool to have.* Cam looked around for a good spot by some jagged metal.

Cam swam over to the opening in the ship. Vera

joined him there. Cam thought the blast site would be a cool place for a photo. The jagged metal might make him look tougher. Cam put his hand on Vera's shoulder. His heart beat faster when she moved closer to him. They waited side by side for his dad to take the photo. Mr. Lund was slow to get to a good spot to take the photo. Cam thought, *take as long as you like, Dad.*

A current of water moved them back and forth. First, the current pulled them away from the ship. Then, it pushed them back again. To Cam, it was like the ship had pushed and pulled him. The last gust of water pushed them to the ship and its jagged metal. Cam bumped the metal with his leg. The bump was quick. He felt the metal, but he did not know the metal cut his leg. Cam looked down at his leg but did not see anything wrong. He couldn't see the small cut. The pressure at that depth kept the cut from bleeding.

Cam looked back at the ship, but he couldn't see anything strange there. He looked back, just in case, as he swam away from that spot. As Cam swam more, blood came out of his cut in very little drops. Not enough to see, but just enough for sharks to smell. Sharks can smell blood in the water up to four miles away.

Faces in the Flames: A Ghost Story

CHAPTER TWELVE

Calling Cam

Cam became more charmed with the ship as the dive went on. The ship seemed to call to him. Maybe the calling was just in his grandpa's past with the ship. Maybe the calling was due to his grandpa's stories. Cam wasn't sure.

At the side of the ship, Cam looked down. From there he saw space between the sand and the deck of the ship. He hoped to see the deck area his grandpa talked about. His grandpa worked on that deck. Cam wanted to go down to the sand to get a good look at it. He signaled to Vera. He let her know he wanted to swim deeper. He wanted to go all the way down to the sandy bottom. Vera made a sad face and shook her head. She knew the dive would have to end soon. She checked her air gauge. The gauge showed she was getting low on air. Cam's tank couldn't have much more either. She made signs with her hand. She showed they could go, but just for a minute.

Cam dove deeper despite the look on Vera's face. Vera did not have a good feeling about things. She had no choice but to stay near Cam. *He is going to get us both in trouble,* kept running through her mind.

Under the ship, they found a gap between the deck and the sea floor. The gap was about 3 to 4 feet. In some places the sand was higher, leaving no open space. They both peaked into that area under the ship. They saw a lot of pipes and valves. The pipes and valves were all red and rusty now. Coral and seaweed covered them. Before the ship sank, oil ran in those pipes to fuel Navy ships. Like the ship, the pipes were all painted gray when the ship was new.

The area under the ship was very dark in some places. The only light came from the open areas at the ship's edge. Deep in the darkness and shadows, Cam saw a bright light. Something was there in the dark. It looked like a flashlight beam. *Could the light be a diver trying to get their attention?* Cam turned and looked up. Vera was about five feet above him. He could see his dad, Tony, and Kai off in the distance.

Cam peered back inside but could no longer see the light. Just then he heard a clanking sound. The noise startled him. Turning, he saw Kai tapping the dull edge of his knife on his tank. Kai did that to get everyone to look at him. Sound goes a long way in the water. The guide pointed up to the surface. Cam knew what Kai wanted, but now Cam was curious. He wanted to see what was making that shining light. Cam felt Vera's touch on his shoulder. She pointed up. He knew he had no choice but to follow her.

The trip up to the surface was a slow one. They could only go up as fast as their slowest bubbles. Cam didn't need Kai to tell him divers need to go up slowly. Cam studied that in his classes. Bubbles from the air tanks go into the diver's bodies. The weight of the water gets less and less as a diver goes up. The less pressure makes the bubbles get bigger. The air must make its way out of the body to be safe. At 15 feet before the surface, Kai stopped everyone. At the 15-foot line was the backup tank they had left. The tank was set up so two people could use it at the same time. If someone ran out of air, the tank was there for them. Cam soon became the one who needed to use the extra tank.

CHAPTER THIRTEEN

Sharks Can Smell Blood 4-Miles Away

Cam did need to use the extra tank. He had been so excited after seeing that light he used up most of his air. He just got to the 15-foot level when his tank ran out of air. His dive gauge started beeping. Cam had never heard the warning tone before. He wasn't sure what the sound was at first. Cam's dad grabbed the gauge before Cam could. His dad gave the gauge a quick look and then turned it to Cam. The boy could see he was almost out of air. By the time Cam could change to the new tank, his old tank ran out of air. He was relieved to get a big breath of air from the new tank. His tense body relaxed a bit after that.

"That was cutting things too close," Cam's dad said as they got to the surface.

"That was amazing," was the first thing out of Cam's mouth. "I can't believe Grandpa was on such a huge ship. Did you see all the damage? The huge chunks of twisted metal!" Seeing the ship thrilled him more than he knew. He forgot about running out of air.

Kai swam up to the two. "Cam, it looks like you are bleeding. We need to get you into the boat." Kai was looking down at the water around Cam.

Before Cam could look for blood, he felt a bump to his fin. Looking down, he saw a large, gray shark swim just a few feet away. Cam swore in surprise. He jerked his knees up to his chest. He didn't want his legs near any sharks.

Everyone helped Cam into the boat first. Vera was next into the boat. Tony followed. Cam's dad got in as fast as he could. Kai stayed in the water with his back to the boat. He watched underwater to make sure no sharks got too close. When two sharks came nearby, he poked at them with the back of his knife. He did not want to hurt the sharks, just keep them away.

"What happened to you down there?" Kai asked Cam. "How did you cut yourself? Did you bump against something down there?"

"That must have been near the spot where the sub hit," he said. "I guess I got cut when the current pushed me back into the ship. I only felt hitting the metal. But, I didn't see anything. I didn't see any blood at the time."

"There is so much pressure that far down. I'll bet you started to bleed closer to the surface."

They helped Cam out of his wetsuit. Blood dripped out of a 2-inch long cut on his leg. Luckily, the cut was not very deep. Kai grabbed a clean t-shirt out of his bag. He held the cloth against the cut. He needed to stop the bleeding. Vera pulled out a first-aid kit. "We'll need the antiseptic*," Kai said. Vera gave the medicine to her dad.

Cam reacted with clenched teeth and a jerk of his head. The antiseptic stung as it went on. Vera kept pressure on the cut while her dad put the bandage on it. Cam chose to watch Vera and not his cut. Before Cam knew it, Kai finished.

"I think you'll be fine," Cam's dad said after Kai finished. "The cut didn't look deep."

After that, Kai pointed the boat back to the island. The weather had gotten worse. The sky was darker again. The water was rougher going back to shore, too. The ship rocked quite a bit.

Cam leaned over to Vera on the way back. He asked, "Did you see the shiny thing under the ship?"

"I didn't see anything," Vera said. "I was mostly watching after you," she said. She sounded bothered.

"Hmm . . . it looked like a light or something," Cam said. "It looked so bright at times, though it was in the dark area under the ship."

"Maybe I was just not looking at the same time you were."

"I guess so," Cam said, his head shook slowly. He could not understand how she could have missed seeing it.

Vera was not sure what Cam thought he saw. She turned to her dad, "Did you ever see any bright light under the ship?"

Kai said, "No, I never have. I've been under the ship a few times. Mostly, just rust or plants." Kai didn't like to hear talk about what's under the ship.

"I want everyone to hear this," Kai said. "Remember, don't go in or under the ship. It's just too dangerous. You're not ready for that yet. There are still things that can fall down and trap you there." He looked at Cam while he spoke. He worried Cam would try to go under the ship.

Cam didn't want anyone hurt. Still, the area under the ship looked safe enough. Cam thought Kai worried too much. True, there were a lot of pipes and not a lot of room between some of them. Though, some places had enough room to go through. Cam wasn't too big for that. Maybe, if he got the chance, he'd go under the ship. *What could be the worst that could happen?*

CHAPTER FOURTEEN

Whatever It Is, It's Calling to Me

When they got back to the hotel, Cam's dad had him take a shower. He wanted Cam to clean the cut with soap and fresh water. He insisted Cam use soap on the wound. Cam didn't like the idea of soap, but he knew it had to be cleaned. Cleaning the cut stung a lot. This time Vera was not there to take his mind off the pain.

After Cam dried off, his dad looked at the cut. Mr. Lund was glad the cut wasn't too bad. There was no need for stitches. Mr. Lund was glad Cam had gotten a tetanus* shot before they left home. The cut stopped stinging before long.

That night, Cam had a restless sleep. At one point, Cam woke up. He thought he heard someone say, "Go get it!" But, when Cam looked over at his dad, his dad was sound asleep. Maybe he had been dreaming a little. Cam thought about the dive and what he thought he had seen. He was still tired. He turned over and fell back to sleep before he knew it. Cam slept but kept tossing and turning. He woke feeling tired.

"How's the leg? Did you sleep well?" his dad asked him. "Every time I woke up, you were tossing back and forth."

"No, not really. The leg's okay. Just a little sore. I'm not sure what kept me awake," Cam said. "I don't think I was awake because of my leg." Cam's dad gave him some pain relief pills.

"Hopefully, that will help. Best thing now is to get some food in you. You'll feel better."

Cam had to be careful on the stairs. He tried not to move his leg too much. He didn't want to loosen the bandage.

The dining area was small, like the rest of the hotel. Once Cam sat down, his dad got him his breakfast. Cam finished off his food right away. His dad took a little longer to finish. Vera and Tony came in just as the two got up.

"Just about ready to dive on the ship again?" Tony asked Cam.

" Or, are you going to stay here and eat all day?" Vera teased.

"I'm on my way now," Cam said. "I've got to say the food here is awesome. The fresh fruit with breakfast is great. I just have cereal in the morning at home." Cam grabbed some fruit left on his dad's plate as they walked away.

The pain reliever and food took Cam's mind off his cut. Cam half-jogged back to his room to get his gear for the dive. Five minutes later he was back and on his way to the beach. They all waited at the boat for him.

"How is your leg today, Cam?" Kai asked.

"Well, not good enough to dance on. But, I never could dance before," Cam joked.

"We taped the bandage up really good," Cam's dad said. "The water should not be a problem. After all, we don't want to attract sharks," his dad said with a smile. Cam didn't see as much humor in it as the others. The idea of sharks didn't make Cam feel so good.

Three of them went aboard the small boat. Kai and Tony pushed it out from the shore. Once more, the motor came to life after a few sputters. Away they went. Kai checked his compass as they went. Again, the group was quiet on the trip to the ship. No one said much.

Cam was busy thinking. He wanted to find out what that shiny thing was. He had a hard time not thinking about it.

It did not take long before they could see the bow buoy in the water. "That buoy sure makes it easier to find the ship, I'll bet," Cam's dad said.

"Yes, it does," Kai replied. "We had a hard time finding the ship until we tied that buoy to it." Kai grabbed the float and tied the boat up to it.

"Be careful down there. The metal can be sharp," Kai warned. "I don't want anyone else to cut themselves. Please think about the sharks we met down there yesterday." Cam didn't need anyone telling him to be careful.

They all got into their scuba gear. Getting ready took less time today. They were used to gearing up in the small boat. The teens flipped backwards into the water at the same time. Going in backwards made sure their face masks stayed on when they hit the water. Soon, Cam's dad and Kai joined the trio* in the water.

Again, Vera swam with Cam. As Cam pulled himself down the rope, he looked over at Vera. He saw a look of thrill in Vera's brown eyes. She shared what looked like a smile through the glass of her diving mask. Cam thought again how lucky he was to dive with the pretty girl.

Cam also thought about what he had seen under the ship. He wanted to see what it was that seemed to be telling him, '*Go get it!*'

Faces in the Flames: A Ghost Story

CHAPTER FIFTEEN

Must Have It

They were almost down to the ship when they let go of the rope. Staying with the rope would take them to the very edge of the ship. They wanted to go closer to where the ship broke in two. That area was 50 feet from where the rope tied to the ship.

The others swam to the spot amid the two halves of the ship. Cam went there but kept inching away. Vera didn't notice him moving at first. Finally, she waved for them to get back to the others.

Cam put his hand to his underwater writing pad. The pad connected to his arm. He wrote, "Just want to see something over there. Won't take long."

Vera knew her dad did not want them to swim away from the group. She hoped they would just be gone for a minute or two. She also hoped her father would not see them swim away.

Cam turned and starting swimming. Vera had to work to keep up with him. She got a little mad when she could see where Cam was going. Before she could catch him, Cam darted under the ship. Vera worried but did not know what to do. She went under just enough to see

Cam. She wanted to be able to go get help if needed. Vera became more upset with Cam as time passed. She kept looking back and forth from Cam to the opening. *What is he doing? He knows he's not supposed to go in there,* she thought. Again, *He is going to get us both in trouble,* ran through her mind. She didn't want to think of how much trouble she could get into. She knew her dad would be mad she let Cam go under the ship. She hoped Cam would get out before her dad found out.

Cam could not get the shiny thing out of his mind. It had been there since he first saw it under the ship. He knew he could go see what it was and get back out in a hurry. As he swam through the opening he spotted the item. It seemed to be near some pipes.

Cam made a quick look back to see if Vera was still there. When he saw her, he was glad she had not left to get her dad. Cam swam on. He had to go around more pipes than he had expected. Weaving by strange shapes started to make him nervous. He kept going anyway.

At times, the shiny thing stopped shining. He kept swimming until he saw it shine again. Cam wondered how long he had been under the ship. The trek seemed to be taking a lot longer than he first thought. With some relief, he got to the object. It hung from a pipe, swaying in the current. A green moss covered much of it.

As soon as his hand closed around it, he felt a slight shock. His impulse was to let go of the object, but he could not. Then, a strong feeling came over him. He felt like he broke into someone's home. *I shouldn't be here,* he thought! Anger and panic filled his head.

With that thing in his hand, he swam as fast as he could to the opening. He was afraid to look back. A quick shudder went through him. Goosebumps ran up his arm. All his efforts went into getting out of there. His breathing was out of control.

Vera swam out from under the ship when she saw Cam coming. She waited there, keeping an eye on Cam. She wished she could see his face, but it was dark under the ship. All she could see was him swimming extra fast. *What's going on?* she thought. *He's using too much air.* He was making a lot of bubbles. That meant he was using a lot of air. At their depth, that meant trouble. Divers have died panicking* at that depth.

As Cam came out from under the ship, a huge shape dropped down in front of him. The shape fully blocked his vision. A hand grabbed out for Cam's dive meter. It was Kai, who had seen all the bubbles. He knew someone was using too much air. The meter said Cam didn't have much air left. Kai dropped the meter and grabbed the strap of Cam's air tank. Kai started pulling Cam up. Cam had to start up that second. The situation had become dangerous!

Faces in the Flames: A Ghost Story

CHAPTER SIXTEEN

Mike

Kai jerked his thumb up, pointing to the surface. Everyone knew right away what that meant. Kai didn't need to tell Cam's dad and Tony to start for the surface.

Kai kept shaking his head left and right. He was angry at the two for having swum off from the group. He was most angry Cam did not watch his air supply. Even in the cool water, Kai started to sweat. He was worried for Cam.

Cam could tell he was in trouble. He knew swimming off from everyone was not safe. That was a big part of his deep-water diving class. He also knew how serious it is to run out of air. *No air and you're a dead man*, Cam thought.

In the rush to get air, Cam forgot about the thing still in his hand. Only on the way up did Cam think about it. He didn't want to take a chance and drop it. He stuck his hand in a canvas bag he kept at his waist and let go. With it safely in his bag, Cam used both hands to share air from Vera's tank. Each tank had a second air hose just in case they had to share.

The safety tank was there at the 15-feet depth. They were all glad to see the tank waiting for them. Cam rushed to switch to the air hose from the new tank. They all had to wait there for 20 minutes. During that time, Cam looked away from his dad and Kai. He couldn't look at them. He knew they were disappointed in him. Finally, the time passed and they could go to the surface.

"What were you thinking down there?!" Kai asked the boy in a very stern voice. "You can't make mistakes like that again! You could have died."

Cam thought not to tell anyone why he went under the ship. He knew he was in a lot of trouble for swimming off. He didn't need to get into any more trouble. He kept quiet.

"I'm sorry," was all he could say. The ride back was even quieter than going there.

Cam only peeked into his bag on the trip back. Everyone but Kai fell asleep on the way back. When Kai was not looking, Cam opened his bag.

In the bag was a flat piece of metal on a thin silver chain. Even with the green moss on it, Cam could tell it was a dog tag. The moss covered the name on the tag, but it was a dog tag. Cam had seen his grandpa's old WWII dog tag before. This was the same shape. He hoped the name on the tag would be readable. *But, how could the tag end up on those pipes under the ship? Surely, after so many years and storms, it would have been lost.*

The trip back to the hotel was very quiet. Cam's dad didn't say much. He was disappointed in Cam for breaking the rules. They all were quiet even when they cleaned their diving gear. Afterward, Cam went off on his own down the beach. He went to find something to use in cleaning off the tag. Cam's dad didn't stop Cam. He thought Cam needed to think about what he had done that day.

The growth on the tag was hard to get off. Cam found a stick on the beach. With it, Cam rubbed and scraped the moss and other sea growth off the tag. Just to read the first name took a bit of work. Stamped on the tag was the name, MIKE. Just a little of the last name was readable. An idea popped into Cam's head. When he got back to the hotel, Cam could use the internet. He knew he could look up the name in the crew list on the ship's website.

Things would not turn out like Cam wanted. As soon as he got to the hotel, his dad told him, "Get ready. There's going to be a show on the island, in our honor. The locals want to do their island dances in their island clothes. They're also having a big feast with lots of food." The internet search for the crew list would have to wait.

The fuss made over Cam and his dad, Bill, flattered* the two. They hoped the people hadn't gone to too much trouble. But, the dancing and feast were not uncommon. The locals were happy to make all their guests feel welcome.

The show was great. Cam had never seen anything like it. The girls wore long grass skirts and danced while some of the boys played drums and chanted. Vera was one of the dancers. Cam thought she was the prettiest one there. He could see Tony pounding out the beat on one of the drums. Also, the food was great. Fish and fruits filled large trays. Cam didn't always like to eat fish. Though, this fish tasted extra good to Cam.

The day was mixed for Cam. It started off great, then went to bad, and back again to great. He was hoping for a good night, but that would not be the case.

Faces in the Flames: A Ghost Story

CHAPTER SEVENTEEN

Dreams Can Come True

Cam had a hard time keeping his eyes open. He wanted to stay awake, but his mind kept drifting off. The day of diving and the feast had taken their toll. As soon as his head hit the pillow, Cam was asleep. Cam had some strange and disturbing dreams. He dreamed he was in a bunk on his grandpa's ship in WWII. Next to him, curled up, was a small dog. A big blast went off and flames flew all around. The ship rocked from side to side. The dog became scared and ran away. In his dream, Cam ran after the dog towards the front of the ship. Then another big blast went off. The dream ended when a big wave of water swept over him.

Cam bolted upright in his bed. The room was dark and still. He felt startled and found he was very wet. *Did someone just throw water on me?* He couldn't see anyone other than his dad asleep on the other bed. *Did I sweat that much during the night?* he thought. He swung his legs over the side of the mattress to get out of bed. His feet landed in a big puddle next to his bed. The water was kind of cold, even though the room was warm. Right away he was wide awake.

He finished in the bathroom and wiped his feet dry.

The thought came to Cam maybe there had been some strange leak from rain overnight. He felt the bed, but it seemed dry. He moved his bed a little just in case. He didn't want a leak in the roof to wake him again. His overall fatigue caught back up to him. Before he knew it, he fell back asleep.

In the morning, he looked down where the puddle had been. A cold shiver went up Cam's spine.

The spot was dry now, but he could see some things there on the floor. Some seaweed and a little sand were on the floor. Cam could also see salt left where the water had dried. *What, or who left water and seaweed there next to Cam's bed?* Cam didn't know what to think.

Cam looked over to his dad's bed, but the bed was empty. Cam's dad was always an early riser. *He must have already gotten up and gone out.* Cam had wanted to ask him about what happened. His question would have to wait a bit.

Cam tossed on some clothes and went down to breakfast. The whole time he was getting ready, he didn't know what he might see. He kept looking back over his shoulder. He was most careful in the bathroom. He knew not to look at the mirror. He didn't want to see some scary face behind him. He'd seen too many scary movies to do that.

Getting out of the room eased Cam's creepy feeling. Cam felt a lot safer when he found his dad. His dad was downstairs, eating. With his dad was Kai. They were busy talking. He recalled how mad his dad and Kai were with him after the last dive. He thought he'd better not barge in while they were talking.

The two had just agreed this day should be a non-dive day. They would take a break from diving. Diving so deep too often is not healthy. Besides, Kai was still upset with Cam for going under the ship. Kai knew how the young diver felt. He could still recall the first time he saw the ship. Kai was amazed at its size. But, the rules were there to protect Cam. He hoped a day of not diving might help Cam follow the rules the next time.

Kai advised Cam and his dad to explore the island. Vera and Tony could be their guides. They could even take them to some of the other islands too.

Before long Vera and Tony showed up. They waited until Cam and his dad were done with breakfast. This time, Lea was with them. Lea would be going around with them today.

Now, as they walked, the island looked different to Cam. During the day, Cam noticed more homes. Kids were playing and people were working on their homes. Something looked out of place to Cam. They all seemed to be doing something, but no one looked busy. The islands had a much slower pace of life. Some of the locals were making hats or bags out of palm fronds. They would tear the plants apart and weave them back together. A woman gave one of the hats to Cam's dad. He put the hat on his head. Cam couldn't help but chuckle a little at his dad.

"What?" his dad asked.

"Oh, nothing. I was just thinking what mom might say if she saw you wearing that hat."

"I'm sure she'd say how utterly handsome I am and faint. Maybe it's a good thing she's not here. I'd have to catch her." A smile came over Bill's face.

Cam gave his dad a low "fog horn" sound. The sound was what he gave his dad when he came up with a bad joke.

Later, Vera and Cam found some time with no one else around. Vera's face changed as she turned to Cam. Her eyebrows had come together more and her lips tensed. Cam could see Vera's mood had changed. She asked him,

"So, why did you go under the ship!? I got into a lot of trouble with my dad. He said I should not have let you go under there. He said I was mostly to blame!"

Getting Vera in trouble hit home with Cam. He liked her too much to want to do that. He was sorry. He didn't even know why he felt he had to go under the ship. He'd soon find out why.

CHAPTER EIGHTEEN

Why Did You Do It?

"I told you, it was calling me," he told her. Then he pulled open the small bag and showed her the object. "It's a dog tag," he said.

"You'd better not let anyone else see that. You were not to take things from the ship. What were you thinking?" Vera said in an upset way. She sure didn't want her dad to find out. Then, her face changed from mad to upset to confused. Only then did Vera process what Cam had said. "That's crazy," she said. "How could a dog get down there?" Vera had never heard the words 'dog tag' used the way Cam meant it. She had only heard of a dog tag as a tag with a dog's name.

The idea of a dog diving down to the ship with Cam came in his head. He couldn't help but laugh out loud. He turned and bent over laughing. "No, it's not a dog tag, it's a dog tag," he said. Right after he said that, he realized the way that sounded. He hadn't thought about 'dog tag' having two meanings.

Vera took a half step back and gave Cam a strange look. "You've had too much time underwater, Cam!" she told him.

Cam could see how he might be looking kind of crazy. He didn't want to look that way in front of a girl he wanted to impress. Also, he didn't want to look like a thief. The more he thought about it, the less he could think of the right way to say that. He didn't know what to say.

He was at last able to calm down. "The tag has the owner's name on it. It has their blood type. Oh, and it has an ID number. It's for people in the service. That's what they call it in the Navy; a dog tag."

Lea came up behind the two and heard just the last part, "dog tag." "Do you have a dog?" she asked of Cam. "I've always wanted a dog, but my mom and dad won't let me have one."

At first, Cam didn't know what to do. He didn't want to tell Lea he had something from the ship. He knew she would tell her dad. So, he just said, "Yes, I have a dog. Since I couldn't bring the dog, I brought its tag with me."

Vera had to turn so she could try to hide her chuckling.

Lea either didn't get it or was okay with Cam's answer. She stopped asking questions about the dog. Some friends called out to her and she waved to them.

"Say, do you think we could get away and use the hotel's computer now?" Cam asked Vera.

"Sure."

The two walked off to the hotel and Lea trailed some ways behind. She was too far to hear them so they felt at ease talking to each other. Cam felt he had to try hard to smooth things out between him and Vera. He kept talking to Vera as they walked. To Cam's relief, Vera soon changed the subject.

After a few more steps, a look of doubt came over Vera's face. "After you go back to your home in the states, are we still going to be friends?" Vera asked Cam.

"Of course! At least, I think we will be," Cam said. Again, he hadn't thought before he spoke. *Did my reply sound as bad to Vera as it just did to me,* he thought?

"The cost to travel to the states is high. My dad wants me to go to college. Maybe I can go to a school in the states. I've been working very hard to get good grades. I hope to get a scholarship That way we could afford school there. Maybe we could visit each other then," Vera said.

"That would be great," Cam said. He'd show his friends he could get a 'hot' girlfriend. He felt quite manly.

A sound broke Cam's train of thought. The dog tag bouncing in his bag had made the sound. "So, do you think we could get Lea to stay here?"

"Don't you know Lea by now? I don't think there's any way we could."

"Yeah, I guess you're right. I just thought I'd ask."

They barely got a few yards from where they were before they had to stop. A large coconut fell just in front of Cam and Vera. "Wow, it's kind of risky walking around here," Cam said.

"Yes, who knows what Tony might drop next?" Vera said. She looked up. Cam looked up to see what she was looking at.

At the top of a tall tree was Tony, laughing. "Oops!" he managed to say between laughs. Tony came down the tree almost too fast for Cam to see him do it.

"How'd you get up there?" Cam asked. "And how'd you get down so fast?" Cam looked for a ladder or rope nearby but he couldn't see one.

"It's easy. You wanna try?" Tony asked.

"Sure!" was Cam's first response. He walked to the tree and looked up and up and up. He started thinking about how far he would fall. "Ah, how do you do it?" he asked. The tree looked very tall.

"I've been climbing trees all my life," Tony said. "I just use my hands and feet. You'd better use this cloth strap.

Tony hopped a few feet up the tree and then came right back down. Then he took the cloth strap and put it around his feet. He showed Cam how to keep his feet inside the circle of the strap. The strap helped give a better foothold on the tree.

Now came Cam's turn. Cam wasn't so sure he could climb the tree. Vera was trying not to laugh. Well, she really didn't try too hard, though. Cam did look a bit worried. He went up to the tree and put his feet firmly on the base of it. He reached up and grabbed the tree then tried to bring his feet up a little. The cloth caught on the rough surface of the tree. Cam found himself on his back on the ground looking up. Vera and Tony were looking down at him.

"Did you want to see me climb up and down, again?" he asked.

"Maybe," Vera said. "That was too fast for me to see. Can you do it slower next time?"

"Great view from up there," Cam said. He tried to reassure the two he indeed climbed the tree. He hoped they weren't going to make him do it for real.

Tony could see Cam wasn't going to be able to climb the tree. He played along. "Yes, quite a view," Tony said while he was looking down at Cam.

CHAPTER NINETEEN

You Can Find Anything Online These Days, Even a Ghost

Cam, Vera, and Lea resumed their walk to the hotel. Lea trailed behind the teens. The walk to the hotel was short. Once there, Cam asked to use their computer. The hotel let him use the computer since he was a guest. Cam went straight to the ship's website. He had been there many times on his computer at home. Here, the PC took forever to open the web page. The computer at the hotel was slow. Cam's PC at home was much faster. Still, Cam had no choice. There were no other PCs around.

After a few minutes, "Look, here's the list of the guys." The thrill in Cam's voice was easy to hear. He found the names of the crew on the website. He got very excited at what he found. "Here is my grandpa's name," he told Vera. He clicked on the name. A photo of his grandpa popped up on the screen. "That's what he looked like when he was just 21 years old." Cam was beaming with pride.

Vera saw Cam looked just like his grandpa did years ago. She said to Cam, "Your grandpa was a very handsome young man. You look so much like him." Cam didn't catch the compliment, but that was ok with Vera. It would embarrass her if he had.

Sadly, as Cam looked at the crew names he saw a lot of guys named Mike. "Oh great. Mike must have been a popular name back then," he said. "I don't think I'll be able to find out who he was by just his first name."

Cam continued to look through the website. He found a picture of all the men on the crew. "At least here's a picture of the dog that was on the ship." Cam pointed to the crew photo. In it, a sailor held a small dog in his arms. "Per the photo, the dog's name is, Salvo. My grandpa told me about a dog that was on the ship. A guy found the dog in Hawaii when the ship stopped there. The dog became the ship's mascot," Cam explained. "That must be him."

"Mascot?" Vera asked, wondering what the word meant.

"Oh, a mascot is a symbol for a thing that brings luck."

"I guess the dog wasn't very lucky in this case," Vera said. She thought about the ship sinking.

"Yeah, I guess you're right, though, it did bring us together." Cam knew he said the right thing when he saw a slight blush on Vera's face. His face got a little hotter, too. He had to look away for a moment.

"Oh, look," Vera said. She pointed to a photo caption the web page. "The page says the owner and the dog both died when the ship sank."

A chill ran down Cam's back and goosebumps broke out on his arms.

"I hadn't thought about that. I guess I should have. Probably a bunch of guys died on the ship's deck. That was right where we were yesterday. But, now the deck is upside down. The owner of the dog tag may have died that day," Cam said. "Maybe, right there!" Pieces of Cam's dream flashed in his mind. Again, in his mind, he saw the blast and flames on the ship.

Silence filled the room. The boy and girl thought

about what had happened years ago. The silence didn't last long. The sound of Lea's voice shocked the two. Their heads spun back to see Lea behind them. Like any little sister, she asked, "What are you two doing?"

Lea's question snapped them back to the moment. Thoughts about the sailor, the dog, and the ship left their heads. They scrambled to think of something to say. They did not want Lea to know about the dog tag.

"Oh, ah, remember when we talked about my dog? It made me think about the dog on board the ship when it sank. I was just showing your sister a photo of the dog," Cam said. He hoped Lea would believe his little lie.

"That was a cute dog," the little girl said. "Is he still alive?"

"No, the website says he died when the ship sank. I guess he never got off the ship."

"I think the sailor must have loved that dog. I would have," Lea said. "He's so cute."

"I'm sure he did," Vera said.

Faces in the Flames: A Ghost Story

CHAPTER TWENTY

Staying in Touch

"Say, here you are." The well-known voice was Cam's dad's. He didn't mean to, but he startled the two teens when he said that. They spun towards him.

"Ah, we were just looking at the ship online," Cam said.

"Yeah, and about a dog," Lea added. Lea pointed to the dog in the picture on the web page.

"Well, you'll get one last chance to look over the ship tomorrow. It's our last dive on her. Your grandpa would be proud of you doing all this, Cam."

"I miss him, Dad," Cam said.

"Me, too," Cam's dad replied, "Me, too." He put his hand on Cam's shoulder. No one said anything for a moment.

Just then, Kai walked through the doorway. "I guess your dad told you about tomorrow."

"Yes, I just started telling him," Cam's dad said.

"The plane will leave at noon the day after tomorrow. There won't be time for a dive on that day."

Cam wished he could have more time on the island. At first, one week seemed like a long time. Now that he had done so much, one week didn't seem long enough. His time on the island was a magical time for Cam. The islands offered so much for him. Vera, diving the wreck, and the dog tag filled his time. Cam's friends, house, and school seemed so very far away. Those things were like a fading memory.

The rest of the day Cam thought about how he could keep in touch with Vera. Vera didn't have a phone. He could email her, but that brought up two problems. Email was only good for a one-sided note. He wanted to be able to see her when they spoke. Also, she didn't have a computer of her own. He was sure the hotel would not let Vera use their PC. She wasn't a paying guest there.

Then an idea came to him. Maybe they could use the school's webcam to talk online. Vera had said she had been on the internet at her high school. If they let her, Cam could talk and see her at the same time. It would be a lot better than just writing an email.

Cam told Vera his idea. "Well, that might not be easy," Vera replied. "I would have to get special permission from the school. The school only has two PCs."

"I'll try to figure a way to help them in return," Cam said. Maybe then they would let you use one of their PC's. I don't know what I can do, but maybe there's something."

"That would be great, but I have to use it after school. If I call you after school, say around 4 pm here in Ulithi, what time will it be for you?" Vera asked.

"Hmm . . . let me figure it out. My time would be 11 at night, but the day before."

"What? How can that be?" Vera asked making a face.

"I know we are 18 hours behind your time. Gosh, too bad we can't bet on a lottery. You could tell me what numbers will win," Cam said. He tried to not laugh too much at his own joke.

"Sure, that will work," Vera said with sarcasm in her voice and shook her head. "Boys!"

CHAPTER TWENTY-ONE

Not Alone Down There

Cam heard the voice and the words, but they didn't make sense. He knew the voice. The words were familiar too, but out of place. *Oh, no. Am I having another dream?* he thought. "Ok, Mister. Out of that rack! Time to rise and shine. Hit the deck." Cam took a few seconds to grasp what was going on. He wasn't dreaming this time.

"Wha, what?" Cam mustered in response.

"Out of that rack! Time to wake up," his dad said again. "Don't you recall your grandpa saying that to you? 'Out of that rack?' He didn't have to tell you very often. That's what they told the sailors on the ship to wake up. A rack was the word for someone's bed."

"Oh, yeah. Now I remember," Cam said, his eyes still shut. "Oh, yeah!" he said, louder this time and more awake. He remembered this was their last day to dive on the ship.

"I don't know if we can go out today," Cam's dad said. He was looking out the window. The morning was dark and cloudy. "We'll get ready and go down for breakfast. We can see from there."

"Ok." Cam couldn't help but be a bit disappointed. He

hoped they would be able to have one more dive."

Cam rushed to get ready and went downstairs with his dad.

The cook for the small hotel was there, as usual, with her big smile. She was like so many of the people Cam and his Dad met on the islands; always smiling. Cam asked what she was serving that day. He was happy to hear the response was pancakes. Cam loved the pancakes on the island. They cut up bananas on them. Cam topped them with a lot of coconut syrup. This was Cam's new favorite meal.

Cam finished in no time. He made sure to use every piece of the pancake to sop up the syrup. An empty dish and a smile on Cam's face were the only things he left. Oh, there were also some sticky fingers.

Again, Kai came in just as the two were finishing their food. "Good morning. I think we will have a good day today. The sky doesn't look good right now, but it should get better as the day goes on. I'm afraid Vera can't come today. She must help her mom and the other ladies on the island. There is one last big feast tonight. It's in your honor. It's tradition to have a feast when our guests are leaving. This way we all get to share a meal with you before you go. After all, we need to give you a good send-off," he added with a smile.

"We'd be honored. Thank you," Cam's dad said.

Cam was kind of bummed out. He wanted one more dive with Vera before he had to go. He hoped she would be able to help him put the dog tag back on the ship. Maybe no one else would find out he had taken it. Without Vera, Cam would have to buddy up with her dad, Kai. There'd be no way he could sneak the dog tag back to where he had found it.

The ride to the wreck was the coldest and wettest of

all. The water swelled 2 to 3 feet up in the air and then back down again. The swells made the boat bounce around. Water sprayed over the bow with each bounce. Without Vera's weight, the boat bounced even more. Nothing was going like Cam had thought it would that day.

"Watch your gauges down there," Kai reminded Cam. Cam didn't need a reminder. The scare he got the other day was enough. The reminder was just one more thing to bug Cam.

Cam did get some good news. Today, Kai paired Cam to dive with Tony. Cam's dad would have Kai as his diving buddy today.

They were all happy to get to the dive site. The trip had been a tough one. The bouncing had bothered Bill's stomach. He was looking forward to being in the water. He knew he would feel better there, under the water.

Everyone went over the sides of the boat at the same time. Tony and Cam went in backward over the left side. In the navy, they call the left side the port side. Kai and Cam's dad went backward over the starboard or right side.

Like other days, they made their way down the rope to the front of the wreck. For some reason, the area by the ship looked a bit scary. At first, Cam couldn't think why. After a second, he saw why. Near the ocean floor, the light was much less than before. The dark sky above made the area by the wreck very dark. The ship was not as well-lit today.

As they swam, Tony seemed to be sticking like glue to Cam. Each time Cam looked at Tony, he was watching Cam. *I guess I deserve this*, thought Cam. *Sure, I swam off from Vera before. Now, Tony expects me to do that to him. And, I'll bet his dad told him to keep his eyes on me.*

The current around the ship was quite strong today, too. It tossed them back and forth. Staying in one place was difficult. The long plants attached to the ship kept rushing back and forth. There almost appeared to be more plants, they were moving so much. The ship was difficult to see.

Mr. Lund felt better, but still not good, due to the strong current. He chose to take things a little easier today. The two dads stayed in the area where the sub had hit the ship. They shined a light into the areas left open by the blast. The strength of the explosion amazed Cam's dad. The blast left parts of the ship twisted and jagged. The sight helped him forget his stomachache.

Cam and Tony swam to the front of the ship to see the gun mount. All around them, the plants swayed back and forth with the current. At times, the plants partly blocked the boys' view of the ship.

Cam looked for Tony to make sure they were still together. At that same moment, Tony flinched with a shocked look on his face. He stopped swimming and then started to back away. Cam grabbed Tony's arm. Holding Tony's arm, he turned his head to see what Tony saw. Cam only caught a glimpse of the open hatch near the gun mount. He did not see anything strange. The plants continued to block much of his view. Cam felt Tony trying to back away more. Out the side of his diving mask, Cam saw Tony pointing. His hand was shaking.

Cam strained to see what Tony had seen and then he saw it, or him? Cam didn't know what it was. *What the . . .?* The sighting confused Cam at first. Cam didn't know why, but his first thought was, *who is that guy in the gun mount?* Then, what he was seeing started to sink in. Cam's eyes got very big. He was seeing a man sitting in the gun mount. The man was wearing a white cap, blue shirt, and pants like sailors wore. But, the sailor didn't have any diving gear on. How could he be there with no dive gear on?

Just then, the sailor turned his head sharply. His head turned as if he had just heard Cam and Tony. He stared at the two boys. Fear surged through Cam's entire body. His arms and legs felt frozen in place for a second. He almost felt he would sink from the weight of his limbs.

But as fast as the two boys saw the sailor, he was gone. When the plants parted, Cam couldn't see the sailor. Cam and Tony managed to quickly backup. All the while, Cam jerked his head back and forth. He wanted to make sure the plants didn't just block his view of the man. He looked back and forth twice between the gun mount and Tony. Tony broke free of Cam's grip. He started to race away.

Cam's fear went out of control after Tony left him. He felt very alone. A peek back, with no sailor there, got Cam moving. He swam as hard as he could to follow Tony.

Luckily, Tony swam right into his dad. Kai had seen all the extra bubbles. He knew something was wrong. Kai grabbed Tony's air tank strap. Kai knew panic that deep is fatal*. With his other hand, Kai reached out to grab Cam's too.

Tony kept pointing back and forth to the gun mount. Tony also kept shaking his head back and forth. Kai eased towards the guide rope. He knew he would need help to hold both boys. Kai looked to Cam's dad for that help. He couldn't hold onto the boys much longer. Cam's dad caught on right away. He grabbed Cam's strap.

Even with the tight grip on the boys, they tried to swim away. Cam was visibly scared. He could not stop staring at the gun mount. He kept looking until he could no longer see the wreck.

The dads didn't have time to think about what scared the boys. They had their own fears now, keeping their sons alive.

Faces in the Flames: A Ghost Story

CHAPTER TWENTY-TWO

Who Was That Guy?

The two dads struggled at first trying to help their sons. They could see their sons shaking from fear. Both boys ran out of air going up the rope. The dads shared their air until they got to the extra tank of air. By that time, the boys had calmed down so their dads could let go of them. The two boys had to share the air there, waiting for their wait time to end. The whole time, the boys kept looking down where the wreck was. As soon as they surfaced, the boys scrambled into the small boat.

Kai and Mr. Lund got into the boat as fast as they could too. They didn't know what the problem was. They just knew they wanted to get out of the water. The two boys were terrified. The dads just didn't know what terrified their sons.

"Let's get out of here. Did you see that man?!" Cam yelled.

"Hold on a minute. A man?" Kai asked. His eyes darted around. He expected to see a boat nearby. That would help to explain seeing a man in the water.

Tony still didn't say a thing. He was going into shock. He just sat in the boat trying to cover his head with a towel.

"Yeah, a sailor in the gun mount!" Cam said, pointing down to the water. "He was a ghost!"

"Take it easy, son. Take some deep breaths," Kai said.

"He's, he's right, Dad!" Tony finally said. His voice was shaky. "First, I saw him in the doorway. Then, a second later, I saw him at the gun."

"Wait a minute, boys," Cam's dad said in a calming voice. "Take a couple of deep breaths." He waited until the boys took a couple of deep breaths. He could see the boys calming down. "Now, tell me all you saw."

Kai was not a superstitious man. Still, he didn't want to take any chances. He untied the rope from the float. "We're getting back to the island now. You tell us the story as we go."

The ride back to the island was difficult. The sky was dark and the sea had become rough. The weather was the worst it had been for Cam and his dad's visit. The boys sat as low as they could in the boat. Cam's dad kept his arms around the shoulders of the two scared boys. He felt the boys should sit quietly for now. Questions could wait until they got back to the hotel. The boys were too shaken up to talk. The further away from the wreck site, the safer the boys felt. Cam's dad kept talking to the boys. He tried to calm them.

They all felt better as the boat slid up onto the beach. The surging tide pushed the boat snuggly onto the sand. When they all got out, the boat floated more onto the shore. Everyone grabbed the sides of the boat. Some men from the beach went to help bring the boat still further ashore. They all grabbed the sides of the boat. They carried the boat up about 20-feet onto the shore. Kai took a rope from the boat and tied it to a coconut tree. He wanted to make sure the tide would not take the boat out to sea overnight.

"Leave the dive gear for now," Cam's dad suggested. "Let's get these boys inside and get them something warm to drink."

They found a spot to sit in the hotel's eating area. Kai sat with the boys while Cam's dad got four cups of hot coffee. The boys held onto the hot mugs while their dads sat next to each of them. The ride back and the hot mugs helped the boys settle down. Just holding onto the mugs helped them to feel better. Some color came back into their faces. When they first got out of the water, the boys were pale.

"Now, tell me, please. What exactly did you see?" Kai asked the boys.

Both boys started talking at the same time. Then, Tony pointed to Cam and said, "You go first."

"Ok," Cam said, "it's hard to say exactly. I was looking at Tony and he looked scared like he had seen a ghost. Then, I looked to see what he was looking at. The seaweed near the wreck was extra thick today. The plants swayed so much. We couldn't see anything for very long. Then, between the plants, I saw this guy in the gun mount. I think he was a sailor from the ship. He just sat there, looking through the gun sight. Just like he was going to shoot at something. But, he didn't have any diving gear on. He was just sitting there."

"Yeah, but I saw him near the door first," Tony said, still shaking. "Then, like Cam said, he was at the gun. Yeah! No gear on. Just sitting there. Then, he turned and looked at us! He just stared."

"Are you both sure about that?" asked Cam's dad. "Kai and I were not far away. I didn't see anything. All I saw was a lot of bubbles coming from you boys. That's when Kai waved me to come along with him. We wanted to see what problem you boys were having."

"This is the first time I've ever heard of a ghost on the ship," Kai said. "And I've taken a lot of people down there."

"Do you really think there were ghosts down there?" Cam's dad asked Kai.

"No, but I'm not sure what happened. Maybe the boys have spent too much time so deep. Divers can get what's called Nitrogen Narcosis. It's like getting drunk, from spending too much time in deep water."

"Yes, we did cover that in our classes. Do you remember, Cam?"

"Yeah, a little," Cam said. He didn't know what to think. It all made sense, but he could have sworn he saw a ghost. Nobody could be down there in the water like that. They'd have to wear diving gear. Also, they couldn't have vanished like that. But, Cam couldn't say for sure. Being down too long may have affected him. The sailor seemed so real. But, could a ghost be real?

CHAPTER TWENTY-THREE

An Answer That Makes Sense

After almost an hour the two dads got the boys calmed down. At the end of the hour, the boys were doubting they saw a ghost. They both thought it was the Nitrogen Narcosis.

"I think we've gone over this as much as we can," Cam's dad said to Kai.

"Yes. You boys should take a little nap before the feast tonight. It's been a long day for everyone. I think I'll take one myself," he said, stretching his arms along with a big yawn.

"Come on, Cam. Kai's right. It's been a crazy long day. Let's have you get a little rest," Cam's dad said.

The boys went off with their fathers.

Refreshed from their naps, Cam and his dad got to the feast. There were a lot of people there. Cam spotted Vera in the crowd. As soon as Cam saw her, he rushed over to her.

Vera looked upset. "Tony told me what happened at the wreck," Vera told Cam. "I'm just glad you both are all right."

"Me too!" Cam said. "But, I could still swear I saw a guy in that gun mount. I just don't know."

"How could a man be down there without an air tank?" Vera said.

Tony saw Cam and Vera through the crowd. He hurried over to them. He still looked a bit shaken up and not his confident self.

"Hey, how you doin'?" Cam asked him.

"I'm okay. Wow, that was crazy weird today," Tony said. Tony's face was still a little pale. Cam wasn't sure Tony was as "okay" as he said he was.

Close by, island music started to play. Vera took both Cam's and Tony's hands. She led the way for the two boys to the feast. As old as the boys were, they did feel safer holding Vera's hands. The music and the smell of the food did a lot to change the mood. With the change of mood, the three teens stopped talking about the dive. Talk became centered on the food. The teens led the way to the tables. Cam's dad trailed closely behind, talking to Kai and his wife. Lea rode on her dad's shoulders.

The feast was amazing and the food was great. Cam enjoyed it. He also liked having to eat the food with his hands. Many kids were in their island costumes. They did many native dances. The feast had the effect Cam's and Tony's dads had hoped for. The boys forgot about the ghost as the night went on. Their thoughts turned to the party.

Later, in their room, Cam, and his dad talked about the party. They were both glad Cam's dad took a lot of pictures. That way they could show friends and family back home what happened. Cam's dad made a point to not talk about ghosts.

Forgetting about the ghost would be short lived.

CHAPTER
TWENTY-FOUR

A Visit in the Night

As bedtime neared, Cam's worry about ghosts came back to him. When the time came for lights out, Cam became uneasy. He really didn't want to be in the dark. He never had to sleep with a light on before. For sure, he wanted to have a light on that night. The thought of the ghost still upset him.

Cam was tired despite his earlier nap. He considered staying up all night, but he would be a wreck in the morning. He thought, *I don't want dad to think there's a problem. Besides, I bet dad wouldn't want to sleep with a light on.* There were no little lights he could leave on. *I think I'll be okay. I am pretty tired.* Cam put his flashlight under his pillow. He felt a little safer as he gripped the flashlight.

At some point, Cam nodded off. In the middle of the night, Cam began to stir in bed. A super bad dream came over him. He dreamt of the ship. In the dream, Cam was in the water. He saw himself swim into the ship, into the dark ship. There were sharp pieces of steel all around him. The pieces of steel formed a cage on three sides. The fourth opened to a wall of seaweed. He knew he would have to swim through the thick undersea forest. Cam started out through the seaweed. He had a hard time seeing anything as he swam. At times, he would bump into old pipes. He swam forward, reaching out with his hands to part the long vines of the plants. As he moved some vines to the side, the back of the sailor's head appeared. The head spun around in Cam's direction. The face was rotting. There were holes in the skin on the face. The skin looked burnt. With the face looking at him, the eyes popped open.

Cam woke with a start. He jerked when he saw that same face looking at him again. The face was mere inches away from his. Its lips were moving. The face was talking or trying to talk. No sounds were coming out of the mouth. Cam froze in fear. He couldn't move.

"Aaahhh!!" Cam finally screamed. With the scream, the face burst like a soap bubble. Cam could feel the water on his face from the bubble. He cringed. He could even taste the salt left on his lips. He brushed his mouth with the back of his hand in disgust.

The face was that of the sailor Cam had seen in the water. The face was old and covered with barnacles. It looked kind of like an old, shriveled apple. Cam's scream had seemed to blow the face away.

"What's the matter?!" Cam's dad called as he jumped up. "What's wrong?" He scanned the room to make sure no one had broken into it.

"He, he, he was here, Da, Dad. I saw him," Cam struggled to say. His voice was trembling. Cam had never been so scared. Underwater, Cam was in the ghost's world. Now, the ghost had come to Cam's world.

"Who was here?" his dad asked, looking around the room.

"The sailor from the ship today," Cam said. "Right there. He was dripping wet." He was right at my face when I woke up.

"Are you sure you saw it after you woke up?" Cam's dad didn't believe it was a ghost. "Tell you what, son. You can sleep in my bed with me tonight if you want. You must have been half asleep when you thought you saw something. There's nothing here."

"Are you sure? Nothing?" asked the shaking boy. Cam looked around the room to make sure.

"Sorry, son, but no one is here. Just you and me." Cam's dad worried about his son. He hoped the deep diving hadn't caused problems.

CHAPTER TWENTY-FIVE

Time to Say So Long

Cam took his dad up on his offer so he would not sleep alone. He hopped into his dad's bed, on the side that was against the wall. He didn't want to take any chances. He also kept his flashlight with him, just in case.

Cam and his dad both knew they needed to get some more sleep. They were going to have a long trip getting back home. Cam clamped his eyes shut and didn't open them again that night. It took him over an hour to fall back asleep. Once he was asleep, he was in a deep sleep. The day and night had been so full, Cam fell asleep, even with his fears.

The sun coming through the window woke up the two. Cam's dad got up first. Cam was still a bit on edge when his dad left him to go into the bathroom. Cam really wasn't sure he wanted to be alone at all. Luckily, there were no more faces in the room. The light of day did a lot to help Cam feel normal.

Other than their diving gear, the two did not have too much to pack. They spent most of their days on the island in swimsuits. So, packing was quick and they went down for breakfast.

Cam was happy to see what they were serving for breakfast. "I love these pancake breakfasts. I don't recall ever having syrup like this at home. Do they sell coconut syrup at home?" Cam asked. Cam seemed to have pushed the ghost from his mind, at least for the moment.

"Yes, actually. I've seen it in the store. We'll get some when we get home. I like it too." Cam's dad was glad Cam's thoughts had moved from the ghost to breakfast.

After a delicious meal, the two got up to go back to their room. As they left their table, Cam said to the cook, "I'm going to miss your food the most." The cook returned a happy nod. The father and son went back to their room for their things. They only had to pick up their bags and head back down the stairs. While in the room, Cam kept looking over his shoulder.

In the lobby were Kai, Tony, and Vera. They were waiting for Cam and his dad. While Kai spoke with Cam's dad, the others went outside to talk.

"How was your night?" Cam asked Tony.

"Actually, I didn't sleep well. I had to have the lights on. How about you?"

"That ghost sailor was there in my face last night. Scared the . . .," but he stopped. He didn't want to use bad words in front of Vera. "Startled me," he went on. "My dad doesn't think I saw a ghost, though. The ghost was dripping wet, but no water was on the floor. Oh, and it was weird. His face just popped like a soap bubble. Then, he was gone. I can still feel the water on my face. The whole thing was so disgusting. I'm still not sure what to do. I still think I saw a ghost."

The sound of the PMA airplane broke up their chat. They looked up to see the plane coming down for a landing.

Cam and Vera looked at each other. They could tell

their time together would end soon. "Promise me you'll video call me when you can," Cam said to Vera. Cam and Vera walked a bit away from the others.

"Of course, I will. I will have to call about 4pm, my time," Vera told him.

"Just try to video call me when you can. I'm at my computer a lot. I'll send back some prints of my dad's pictures as soon as I get back. I know it's not easy here on the island to print pictures. He took a lot of pictures. There's gotta be some good ones," Cam said.

Kai, Cam's dad, and Tony put the bags into the plane. Cam gave Vera a quick hug. Vera was happy to end Cam's visit with the hug. In her heart, she knew she and Cam would remain friends. But, more than likely, they would not meet in person again. She gave him a quick kiss on his cheek. Cam thought, *Great, of all the times for dad to stop taking photos.*

"Have a safe trip, Cam," Tony said as he walked up. "I'll talk to you when Vera webcams you."

"That'd be cool. Thanks. And hey, let me know if you see that guy again."

Sitting in the plane, Cam was a mix of emotions. He was sad his time on the island had to end. Getting on the plane was hard since he might never get to come back. On the other hand, she had given him a kiss. He was starting to miss Vera and the island.

He didn't mind saying goodbye to the ghost. He would find out later he didn't have to say goodbye to the ghost. The ghost wasn't being left behind.

CHAPTER TWENTY-SIX

You're Not Home Free Yet

"Sit back and relax," the pilot told Cam and his dad. "As you know, getting back to Guam will just take an hour. Did you have a good trip so far?"

"Yes, our visit was great," Cam's dad started out. Then he started to tell the pilot about the whole trip. Cam kind of tuned that out. He wanted to tell the pilot, *I had the time of my life*. Sadly, he could just stare out the window as the plane rose into the air. Thoughts of the past week filled his head. While he was thinking, the steady sound of the engine took its toll. Cam fell asleep.

At first, Cam thought his dad was shaking him awake. The small plane's lurching up and down was what woke him. He was glad to have gotten some extra sleep but wanted more. He enjoyed not thinking of the ghost. Then, Cam's focus turned to the lurching plane. *What was happening now?* he thought.

The pilot changed some of the plane's settings. Once again, the plane flew in its normal way. "I'm not sure what was wrong," the pilot said, "but I fixed the problem. Maybe just a little 'gremlin,'" he joked. He tried to smile at his joke. The joke didn't work. He still looked a little troubled. Cam was sure the gremlin was really the ghost. With any luck, the gremlin will keep quiet. After that, Cam couldn't close his eyes. He kept watching the vast empty sea below.

The rest of the trip to Guam went smoothly. For Cam, the trip became a blur. He and his dad flew for an entire day. Their connecting flights left them little time to wait at all. They had to run to catch their next flights. Their last plane landed early in the morning. They were at last back in their own state. They had flown through the night. Their huge adventure had ended.

"Cam, I'm so glad we were able to do this together," Cam's dad said. "We had an amazing trip. I will always remember it."

"Thanks, Dad. It was all because of you that we went on this trip. You got us to take SCUBA lessons. Also, you made all the plans to get to Ulithi," Cam said.

"Well, the real person to thank would be your grandpa. He was the reason for the trip." Cam and his dad sat there in the plane for a few minutes. They got up and gave each other a hug. Then, they slowly gathered their bags and got off the plane. Both Cam's dad and Cam were so happy to see Cam's mom. She was waiting for them in the airport. Cam's mom drove her travelers home.

"I will be happy to sleep in my own bed tonight," Cam's dad said. "The hotel was nice, but the bed wasn't mine."

Cam didn't say anything about his bed. He, on the other hand, worried about being in his own bed.

After Cam walked in the house, he had a funny feeling. The house looked different to him. Yes, everything was there and in its place, but things looked odd. He felt he was seeing his house for the first time. He wasn't sure if it was because of the ghost, or what.

Cam felt better when he heard his dad say, "Gee, the house doesn't look quite the same. But, that's like that each time I travel for work. I wonder why?"

Cam was relieved. He thought it was just him, or rather, the ghost.

Cam's mom made breakfast for her two travelers. "As much as I liked the food on the island, yours is better," Cam told her. Mr. Lund was glad to see the big smile come to Mrs. Lund's face when Cam told her.

The rest of that day was busy. The first thing they did was go over the entire trip with Cam's mom. She wanted to hear about all the things they had done. Showing Cam's mom all the photos took a long time. She was glad her 'boys' had shared such an adventure. She was also glad to not have been on such a long trip. She didn't care to fly so much.

Cam gave her the wrapped present he pulled from his suitcase. She liked the necklace he had bought for her on the island. Cam also showed her the cool seashells he had found there. "I'll have to find a special box to keep these in," she said to Cam.

The excitement of being home kept Cam going most of the day. Then, Cam started to nod off at dinner. Later, he felt in a daze when he talked to some friends on the phone. Cam tried to stall going to bed but knew he couldn't stay up all night. He looked at the clock. He could hardly believe the time was only 8 p.m. He didn't want a visitor that night. Cam got lucky. He fell into his bed right away. Before his head hit the pillow, Cam was asleep. Cam slept soundly throughout that first night back. Nothing could have woken him up, not even a ghost.

Faces in the Flames: A Ghost Story

CHAPTER TWENTY-SEVEN

Welcome Home

Cam was not so lucky the second night. He felt he could get through the night without a light, so he did not look for one. Cam felt safer in his own room. Plus, the bathroom was just outside his bedroom door. This bathroom always had a small, dim night light. His mom liked to have the light there. His parents' room was just next to the bathroom door. *Maybe the ghost didn't come back home with me*, he thought. *Maybe*. He hoped.

Once again, Cam did not sleep well. He had dreams. He kept having dreams about the ship and his dives. He went back into the dream he had on his last night on the island. Again, in the dream, he came face to face with the ghost sailor. Again, he woke up with a start. He did a quick scan of his room. Next, he looked out into the hallway. He was glad to see the glow from the night light in the bathroom. Right away, the light made him feel safer. Not safe, but at least safer. He shuffled over and used the toilet. Again, he made sure not to look in the mirror. But, when he reached for the handle of the faucet, he saw it. 'It' was a reflection on the faucet spout. The image was too small to make out exactly. All he could see something blue and white at the top. This time, he wanted to be ready. As he turned his head to see, he reached over and flipped the light switch. The bright light blinded him for just a split-second. He could just see the blue shirt of the sailor and his white cap. The image changed into a face of smoke, then vanished. It was as if a breeze blew the smoke away from his eyes.

"Ahh!" He cursed. Frightened, he followed his first instinct and called out, "Dad!"

Cam's dad quickly sat up in bed. He called out to Cam, "Is everything okay?" He worried that Cam was still having problems from the deep dives.

"Ah, yes, it's okay. I was just surprised to wake up in the bathroom. Must have been sleepwalking. It's fine. 'Night." Cam didn't want to get his dad or mom upset. After all, what could he tell them? Would they believe his story? His dad didn't seem to believe him the other times. Also, if he told them about the ghost, he would have to tell them about taking the dog tag. He didn't want to have to do that.

Cam was glad to get back to his own bedroom. He felt a little safer there than in the bathroom. After he shut the door, he put a towel along the floor. Then, with the light on, Cam lay in bed with the covers up to his chin. He felt like he was 4-years old and afraid of monsters in his room. He would jump up onto his bed to make sure no monsters could grab his legs. Tonight, Cam did the same thing.

The night turned out to be a long one for Cam. In the morning, his mom let him sleep in later than normal. She thought he might still be tired from the trip. Little did she know Cam was scared awake most of the night. In truth, he managed to fall asleep closer to dawn.

CHAPTER TWENTY-EIGHT

We're Not into Voodoo

Cam felt so much better when he woke up and saw the sun out. Even still, he knew the day would go by slowly. He watched the clock until the time he could video call Vera. This call was the first time since he left the island that he could talk to her. He was a little nervous. He felt like he knew her well. But, how well could you get to know a person in just a week? Maybe things had changed between the two.

Cam tried to start the video call, but the call did not work the first time. He tried a second time and made the connection. In a flash, Vera's face came on Cam's computer. He could see a look of surprise on Vera's face. Her surprised look turned into a big smile.

"Hi. How are you doing?" he asked her. The signal didn't come right away. The screen took a few seconds for her response. Cam felt like he was right there next to Vera. He didn't know he also had a big smile.

"This is so cool. I'm fine.

How was the trip home?" she asked him. Vera looked thrilled to see Cam on the computer. She had never talked to a friend so far away before.

"The trip was long and boring. The best part about it was I slept through most of the way home. If I was the size of my dad, I wouldn't have been able to sleep so well. The seats are so small." He felt a little awkward. He wasn't too sure what to ask or say. Seems like when he was there he had no trouble thinking of things to say. Now talking wasn't as easy.

"Is that your room I see behind you?" she asked.

"Yeah. Here, I'll move the camera around so you can see it." Right away he was sorry he was showing her his room. He forgot his room was a mess. Usually, his room didn't look too bad. Today was the worst it had been in a while. He had dropped all his things from the trip on the floor when he got in. He hadn't put things away like his mom had asked him to do. "Well, this is my room." He tried to keep the camera from showing the floor. Also, he zoomed past the unmade bed.

He waited a bit but couldn't hear her say anything. He worried she thought he was a slob.

"Wow, nice," she said. There had been a delay in the video cam. "I didn't know you were rich."

"Rich? We're not rich," Cam said. Then, he thought about how much he did have. Compared to Vera and Tony, he does have a lot of things. "Well, I guess we're lucky to have so much. My mom and dad both work so that helps." He didn't know what else to say.

"You are very lucky in some ways, but I'm glad to live where I do. Every day we have the sun and the nice winds. The trees and flowers are lovely. Underwater, we get to see the vivid* colors of the fish. I think we have a little more 'natural' wealth, maybe."

Cam could understand what she meant. "I think you are right," Cam replied.

Vera didn't want to just talk about who has what. She

could tell Cam was a little uneasy. She tried to change the subject. "Tony told me more about that last day you two dove on the wreck. I think he's just about gotten over his fear. Though, I am sure he won't dive there soon. He said he hasn't seen anything since. How 'bout you?" she asked.

"Really? He hasn't seen anything weird since then?" Cam asked. "I've seen that guy a couple times. First, in dreams and again last night, in my bathroom, in person! I turned the light on and he just kind of fizzled away. Creepy! I keep looking over my shoulder now, thinking I will see him."

"Cam, I've been thinking. Do you think it might be the dog tag you took back with you? Maybe the tag is cursed or something. After all, Tony didn't take a thing and the sailor isn't after him."

"Nah, how could it be cursed. Didn't Tony see the ghost, too?"

"Yes, but he was with you when he saw it," Vera said.

"I don't believe in curses and things like that. Are you sure there's no voodoo from the islands going on?"

Vera got a little upset at what he said. "Voodoo thing from the islands?" she asked. "How can you say such a thing? We don't have voodoo things here. We go to church just like you do.

Cam could hear how upset Vera was by the sound of her voice. "Gosh, I'm sorry. I shouldn't have said that," Cam said. "I know you don't believe in voodoo."

"Thank you," Vera said. "Now, did you find anything more about the dog tag? How about the sailor who owned it?"

"I haven't had time yet. Most of the time since I last saw you was spent just getting home," he said. "The trip took forever."

"Well, what do your parents think about this ghost that's haunting you?"

"I haven't told them about the ghost yet. I don't want to freak them out. Besides, I know my dad. He didn't want anything taken from the ship. I would be in so much trouble."

Cam could see the look on Vera's face change. At first, she had looked happy to see him. Then, she looked a little letdown. That was when he said he didn't know anything new.

"You know my dad told us all not to take anything. Why did you do it?" Vera asked. Now she looked a little annoyed.

"I don't know. Even now I can't recall going under the ship. I just kind of found myself there with it. I was okay with just having photos. When I saw the tag, it seemed to call to me.

"I think the tag has stopped calling to you. Now it's more like shouting and shaking fists," Vera joked.

CHAPTER TWENTY-NINE

A Friend Who's into Girls and Ghosts

"You may be right," Cam said. "This is sure going to take some looking into. My friend John is coming over later. He's into ghost hunting. He looks for haunted houses. He watches those ghost hunting TV shows all the time. Maybe he will have some idea of what's going on."

"I hope so. Cam, I've got to be getting off now. They won't let me be on the computer too long. Besides, the weather here is looking worse. We've had nothing but bad weather since you left."

"Oh, okay. By the way, I'll be able to get to those pictures soon. I have not forgotten."

"Thanks. Talk to you tomorrow?" Vera asked.

"No problem. See you then. Bye." Vera reached to her keyboard and the call ended. *At least she was smiling when she had to go*, Cam thought.

Cam sat there a minute thinking about what she had said. *Are the visits connected with the dog tag? How will I know?* A few minutes later, the doorbell rang. Cam heard his mom yell up to him, "Cam, your friend, John, is here."

Cam yelled back, "Can you send him up to my room, Mom?"

Seconds later, John stepped into Cam's room. John wore his usual black t-shirt and jeans. He was tall for his age and very thin. His black clothes made him look even thinner than he was. Cam took some things off a chair and tossed them onto the floor. As John sat in the chair, his blond hair fell across his face. Hooking the strand behind his ear, he said, "Hey, man. How was the trip? Get anywhere with hot girls there?" John didn't expect Cam had met any good-looking girls. Cam's answer surprised him.

"In fact, there was this one pretty girl. I hung out with her every day," Cam said with a nod of his head. "I was just talking with her a few minutes ago." His face went a little red at the thought of Vera.

"Cool. You didn't post any pictures yet, how come?"

"Internet time was hard to get over there. They are low-tech over there. The only computer I could find was in the hotel. Also, the net kept dropping off. But, I have them right here on my computer now. I'll show you." So, Cam started to show John the photos from his trip. He showed him photos of the islands, the hotel, and the people they met. John liked the photos of the ship. He thought the ship looked creepy. He liked the photos of Cam and Vera. Vera impressed him.

"Wow, she is hot!" John said. "So, are you in love now?"

Cam had to think about it. He did like Vera, but he didn't think they were in love with each other. "No, I don't think so. Also, we won't be able to afford to go back for a long time. The trip was expensive. And, she's not going be able to come out here. She'd have to get a major scholarship. I don't think a romance could work out. But, you never know."

"I suppose you didn't bring much back?" John looked a little letdown. He was kind of fishing for a present for himself. But, he saw Cam hadn't brought back much. It looked like Cam only brought back a hat, a bowl, and a shell necklace. John guessed that those things were all made by hand on the islands. John felt the photos with Vera were Cam's best keepsakes.

After Cam shared the photos, he told John about the dog tag. "I did get this while I was there. The tag was sitting under the ship, just hanging from a pipe."

"Wow, that's cool. It was on the ship?" John asked.

"Yeah, just hanging there and in a dangerous part of the ship. The diving guide didn't want me to go there. Said that area was too dangerous. To be honest, I still don't know why I went to get the tag." Cam held the tag by its chain and handed it to John. "Take a look."

"Ouch!" John said. "I just got a shock when I touched the chain."

"Yeah, seems to come with the chain," Cam said, half-jokingly.

John held the tag so he could read it. "Oh, wow. You can even make out the name. Do you know who this guy, Mike, is? Here, you can scrape off a bit more and we'll see the last name too." John chipped a piece of the coral off the tag.

"Oh, wow. Looks like his last name is Bowers. I guess the tag is easier to clean off now that it's dried out some more." Cam was happy to see the sailor's last name. There were a lot of sailors on the ship.

"Here. Let's check this out on the ship's website. He might be in the crew photo. Here's his name in the crew list." Cam pulled up the website for the ship. Then, he clicked on the crew list and found the sailor's name. Mike's name had a link on it. When Cam clicked it, Mike's photo came up on the screen. Goosebumps raced up Cam's arms. The hairs on the back of his neck stood up.

He could see the dog tag belonged to the ghost!

"What's going on? What's wrong?" John asked seeing Cam's reaction to the photo.

Cam looked kind of in shock, but got out, "My ghost!"

CHAPTER THIRTY

That's My Ghost!

"Your ghost? You've got your own private ghost now? Since when?" John asked. "I thought you didn't believe in ghosts.

"I knew this would get your attention. I didn't believe in ghosts before, but I sure do now. I know you're into that 'ghost hunting' thing. You'll be interested in this, for sure."

"Yeah. It's cool. There are some haunted places for sure. All kinds of things happen there," John said. "Now things are happening here? So, tell me what have you seen? Has he been in your room? Is he here now?"

Is he here now? The question echoed around in Cam's mind. "Gosh. I never thought he might be here at all. I know I've seen him at night, but could he be here without me seeing him? Do you think he's here somewhere? How would I know?" Cam looked around his room. The idea of the ghost being there anytime gave him the creeps.

"I guess he could be here without you seeing him. I don't think they always show themselves. Maybe he's just chillin'," John said. "What else do you know about this guy?"

"Not much. The website said he worked in the ship's engine room. Oh, and he had a dog on board the ship. The site says he's the one who found the ship's mascot. The dog's name was Salvo."

"Do you know anything about how the guy died?" John asked. "That's always important. Sometimes they just want to go on, but the way they died holds them back.

"Not really. I never knew details about how guys died. I just know a suicide sub hit the ship. A bunch of guys died from that explosion. Maybe there's more on the website."

Cam paged through the website with John. There were a few new pages there that Cam had not seen before. The whole website meant more to Cam now that he had been to the ship.

"Here are photos of the ship burning," Cam said to John. As Cam went through the photos, one stood out right away. The photo showed the ship and a huge cloud of black smoke. The smoke was curling up from the burning ship. Thick smoke covered most of the ship.

"Whoa!" John said. "How could anyone live through that? Do you see those faces in the flames?" John ran his finger around an area on the screen. He outlined two faces he saw.

Cam had just seen the flames and smoke before. Now, he could start to make out faces. They kind of popped out of the screen when John outlined them with his finger. They looked like big faces formed in the smoke coming from the burning ship. "I never saw those two faces before," Cam said.

"That's so weird," John said. "Oh, wait! There's another one." The more the boys looked at the photo, the more faces they could see formed in the flames. "It's like the spirits of the dead were rising with the flames," John said. That sure gave Cam the creeps.

"Wow. If I had seen that before . . . I don't know if I'd have gone down to the ship," Cam confessed.

John asked a few other questions. "How many guys

died on that ship?" John asked.

"Oh, yeah. I think my dad told me the number, 63," Cam answered. "Not all died on the ship. Some died in the water and some died in the hospital."

"That's a lot."

"Yeah. My grandpa was one of the lucky guys," Cam said. "He was brave, too!"

"What'd he do?" John asked.

Cam leaned back, ready to tell the whole story. "When the sub hit the ship, he went to his battle station," Cam said. "He stayed there for about 15-minutes. The ship was blowing up all over during that time. The Captain came by and told my grandpa to get off the ship. He said the ship was going down. Then, my grandpa yelled over to the guys near him to get off the ship. When they got to a hallway, it was filling up with smoke. My grandpa's chief told him, "make sure everyone got out." He had to go back to the boiler room door. When he got there, he yelled in to see if anyone was still in there. There were no answers from the boiler room. He knew if anyone was still in there the smoke would have killed them by that time. Then, he heard a guy yelling. The guy yelled that the ammo was blowing up at the back of the ship. Grandpa didn't know what to do. Then the thought that he would die went through his head. They would tell his mom that her son was dead. As he thought that, he saw a guy run through the smoke. The guy was running a different way. My grandpa thought if that guy could get off safely, maybe he could too. So, he followed the guy through the ship. Then, they got to the edge of the ship. They went over the side and into the water from there. They had to swim through the oil before the flames spread over it."

"Wow, that must have been so scary to be there. The photos looked scary enough."

The two boys talked a lot more about the ship and viewed the website. They lost track of the time. They talked until almost dinner time. John called his mom to ask if Cam could come over for dinner with them. He also asked if Cam could spend the night. She said it would be fine.

Cam had mixed feels about sleeping at John's.

CHAPTER THIRTY-ONE

Who Was in Your Room?

"My mom says you can eat dinner at our house tonight. She also said you could spend the night if you want," John told Cam.

"Sure, that'd be great. Thanks," Cam said. "I'll check with my mom, just to make sure it's okay with her." Cam called down to his mom to ask her. She was a little sorry to say yes. Cam had been gone on his trip for a while. She had missed having him home but knew he wanted to hang out with his friends.

A bunch of thoughts ran through Cam's mind. He was not too sure about spending the night at John's house. He worried the ghost might visit him there. But, maybe John would see the ghost if it did come. Also, he was happy to get out of his own room that night. Cam was certain the ghost would look for him at his own house.

Cam grabbed his pillow. Off he went with John over to John's house. John lived close enough to walk there.

The two boys stayed up past midnight before they went to bed. Cam had not gotten a lot of sleep the night before. At least he had been able to sleep in late. He was nodding off now as he and John watched a movie in John's room. John had a pad and some sheets Cam used as a bed. The pad wasn't very comfy. It was a little narrow and too soft. Still, having a friend in the same room made Cam feel safer.

Cam woke up with the sunlight shining on his face. He looked at his cell phone and saw it was already 9 a.m. He felt good he had slept all night without seeing any ghosts. He knew he could handle things better now.

John's house was quieter than Cam's in the morning. That made Cam recall John's mom would be at work in the morning. He decided not to wait for John to wake. He thought to go home for a cooked breakfast from his own mom. John was still sleeping when Cam quietly left to go home.

As Cam walked through the doorway of his house, he called out, "Mom, I'm home."

"What do you mean, you're home?" she called out from the kitchen. "Where were you? I know you asked about sleeping over at John's house. After I heard you in your room last night I figured you changed your plans."

Cam knew right away things had not been right last night. He stashed his pillow by the couch. He was just in time. His mom came out from the kitchen.

"I tried your door, but it was locked. Then I heard you answer me." A look of fright flashed in Cam's mom's face. "It was you, wasn't it? Who was in your room?!"

Cam followed his mom as she went up the stairs and right over to his room. She waited next to the door while Cam went to open the door. Cam tried turning the knob, but it was locked. Cam's mom took the pass key that was always up on the door frame. She went right for the lock, turned the key and swung the door open. They both were uneasy about what they might find in the room. They each had their own reason.

A big rush of cold air blew past them as the door opened. Chills raced up and down their arms. They saw the window was open. The end of the curtain fluttered out the window. That was the first thing they saw.

The next thing they saw was that EVERYTHING was in its place. Cam's room had never looked so neat. Someone had even made his bed. They made the bed in a military style. They tucked the sheets under the mattress. His clothes, normally heaped on the floor, were put away. They even folded them. As a rule, Cam was bad about putting his things away. He was even worse about making his bed.

Lastly, they noticed the smell. A sweet, but strong smell of oil filled the air. Cam had smelled that before. Cam's dad walked up behind the two. His first words were, "What happened here?" He had never seen Cam's room so neat. "What's that smell? Smells kind of like oil. Where have I smelled that before?"

Cam's dad knew what car oil smells like. The oil smell in Cam's room was different. Suddenly, Cam's dad turned and went off. "Be right back," he said. "I've got to get something."

CHAPTER THIRTY-TWO

Coming Clean

Mr. Lund reappeared with a little bottle in his hand. He opened the bottle and waved it under Cam's nose.

"Oh, wow. That's the smell," Cam said. Cam's mom nodded her head up and down. The odor had a strong oil smell but had a sweetness to the scent.

"It's the special oil that was on your grandpa's ship," his dad said. "The oil was just sent to me by the reunion people. I smelled it when I got it, but I resealed it. How did that smell get in your room?" Cam's dad asked. "And, who cleaned up the room?" he asked as he looked around.

"Well, I guess maybe some of the smell got on my stuff from our trip. And, er, before I left to go to John's house, I thought to clean up my room. John helped some. I guess I got into all the navy stuff we saw," Cam lied. He didn't want his mom and dad to learn about the ghost yet. He thought he could still figure things out without worrying them. Also, he still didn't want them to know he had taken the dog tag. He was kind of happy with himself that he could think up the lie so fast. But, deep inside, he knew that wasn't right. He tried to defend the lie in his mind that this kept his mom and dad safe.

"I guess I must have left the door locked and the wind blew it shut while I was gone." Cam's mind raced for more reasons. "I'm not sure what you heard. I must have left some music on."

"Oh, okay," Cam's mom said. She wasn't sure if she should worry about the change in Cam, or not. *Maybe the trip did him some good*, she thought. *He seems to be more responsible now.*

Cam went on his computer as soon his mom and dad left him. He looked over the ship's website in more detail. Later in the day, his friends, John and Katie, came to his house. Katie was quite a contrast from John. She was a good-looking girl who stood about five feet tall. She dressed nicely and always wore bright colors. But, Katie was into ghosts, just like John. The two of them were, in fact, in a club for people who looked for ghosts. Cam, like most kids at school, thought ghost hunting seemed silly. Lately, he had reasons to change his mind about it.

CHAPTER THIRTY-THREE

That Room's Too Clean to be Yours

"Whoa, what happened here? Your Mom make you clean up your room, Cam?" John said as he caught his first sight of Cam's clean room. "I've never seen you clean up room this much. I've never seen anyone clean their room this much." *I'll be looking for help from you next time my mom makes me clean my room*, he thought.

"No, I had some help with this," Cam replied. "Actually, you helped . . . in case my mom asks." Then he sat down on his bed while John sat at the chair at Cam's computer. John didn't want to sit on Cam's bed. The bed looked too neat. He didn't want to mess it up. Katie sat on a chair in the corner of the room. Cam told them how he came home to find his room like that. He also told them how he had told her John helped him.

"That's amazing," Katie said. "So, do you have the dog tag here still? Can I see it?"

"Yeah, it's in my desk drawer." With that, he pulled open the drawer to get the dog tag. The two friends watched Cam yank his hand back from the open drawer. John and Katie jumped up to see what happened.

"What's wrong?" Katie asked.

A puzzled look was on Cam's face. "There's only supposed to be one!" Cam said. Cam had expected to see one dog tag in the drawer. What surprised him was there were now two dog tags in the drawer. The one he brought back was there on its chain. Another one sat next to it, but not on a chain. "Whose is that and how did that tag get in there?" Cam said. "This keeps getting weirder and weirder."

Cam picked up the second dog tag. He turned it over so he could read the name on the tag. He wasn't sure what to make of a second tag. "Grandpa? How did your dog tag get in here?" Cam asked seeing his grandpa's name on the tag.

John didn't see a problem and sat back down. Katie stayed next to Cam. "You didn't put that tag there?" she asked.

"No, this is always in my dad's dresser. He always keeps it there with some other stuff from my grandpa. There's no reason for that tag to be here."

"That help I said I got cleaning my room, that was from Mike," Cam told his friends. John and Katie looked at each other. They both raised their eyebrows at the same time and nodded.

"So, for sure, the helper was Mike the ghost," John said.

"I don't like that," Cam said. A shudder ran through his shoulders. "He's gone through all my things and even went through my parents' things. That's just creepy."

"I know how you feel. It reminds me of when I was little. Someone broke into our house. I found all my clothes over the floor in my room. I wanted to get all new things after that," Katie said.

Cam was glad Katie could put his feelings into words. He felt they knew each other better.

"Can we see Mike's dog tag?" Katie asked.

CHAPTER THIRTY-FOUR

Pet Allergies

Cam pulled Mike's dog tag and chain out of the drawer. He then dropped them into Katie's hand. He could see she got a jolt when she touched the tag. Katie did not say anything, but John gave Cam a nod. He had seen her reaction too. "Welcome to the club," John joked.

Katie turned to go to back to her chair. John noticed a bunch of dog hair on the back of her clothes. He took a quick glance at the chair. Trying to be a little funny, he teased Cam saying, "I see he missed a spot (to clean). You guys just get a dog or cat?"

"We don't have any pets," Cam said. My mom's allergic. Why'd you ask?"

"Katie's back is covered in pet hair, that's why."

"Who, me?" Katie returned a probing glance. "My dad is allergic too. That's why we've never had any. Where'd I get that?"

"The back of you is covered with dog hair," Cam pointed out.

"I wonder where all that hair came from," Katie said.

"That hair must be from you," Cam said. It wasn't

there yesterday when I tossed some of my clean clothes there."

"No, my clothes were clean when I came over here. Maybe your friend from last night had some on his sheets," she half-joked.

"Maybe the guy from ship brought his dog with him last night," offered John.

The three kids looked at each other. John was half joking when he said that. The reality of what he said hit them all at the same time. Goosebumps spread on all of them.

The energy in the room went up a few notches. The speed of the chat also picked up. "You say the ghost had a dog?" Katie asked. "Are you sure?"

"Sure I am," said Cam.

"Yeah, I saw the dog in the picture with the ghost," John added.

"Let's see that picture. Where'd you get a picture of the dog?" Katie asked.

"There's just a couple of pictures of the dog. In the crew photo, the guy whose dog tag I have is holding a dog. I don't think he would be holding the dog if it wasn't his," Cam said.

"I'm sure you're right," Katie said.

Cam replaced John at the computer chair. In less than a minute, Cam opened the ship's website. He pulled up the photo of the dog. "Here's the photo."

Cam zoomed in on the picture of the dog. He looked at the black and white photo for a minute. "Yep, I'd say that hair could belong to the dog in the photo. Hard to tell since the photo is in black and white. I sure wish it was in color."

"My mom's friend has a dog that looks like the same

breed of dog as in the photo. That dog's hair is about the same color," Katie said.

"Well, you're lucky that the ghost dog is house trained. He could have left you a big, smelly gift on your rug," John said. Katie laughed. John's joke sounded funny to her.

"Oh, yeah," Cam said, thinking how bad the spot could have smelled. How would he have ever explained that to his mom and dad? The worried look on his face made Katie laugh even more.

CHAPTER THIRTY-FIVE

The Missing Link

The three friends sat there looking at photos on the website. They looked at a wide mix of photos. Some were pictures of the ship when it was brand new. Others were of the sailors who were on the ship. Most were photos of the ship sinking. Katie was most amazed at the photo of the faces in the smoke and flames. They searched the photos to find more about the owner of the dog tag.

"What are we missing? What is the link? Is the link with you, the ghost, his dog tag, his dog . . .?" Katie asked.

"I can see why the ghost is at my house. It's easy. I have his dog tag!" Cam said with an 'of course I know' look on his face.

"Yes, but you said the tag was under the ship and easy to see. You also said Vera's dad had been under the ship. He never saw the dog tag before." Katie walked back and forth a couple of times. Each time she rubbed her chin with her hand. Katie didn't look the same now to Cam. Maybe because she had always been so quiet before. Always just in the background. Now, she seemed to be taking charge of the situation. "Do you think the ghost wanted you to find his tag for some reason? Seems like he didn't want Vera or her dad to find it. If he did, they probably would have seen the tag before."

"Now we have to figure out a few things. One - why you? Is it your link to the ship, or your grandpa's? Or, is there something you can do? You know . . . some reason to bring the dog tag here. I don't think the ghost means to harm you. I mean, the guy even put your boxers away," Katie said. "So far, he's just scared you by being here. He's never hurt you."

"Sure, he's been a great pal to me," Cam said, making a wisecrack. "He's only scared me half to death. Though, it could be a lot worse." Cam wondered what the ghost would do if he wanted to hurt him. The options gave him a shiver up his back.

"I'll say," John said. "Cam, we need to know more about the ship than the photos on the web. I saw there is a book for sale on the website about the ship. Did you or your dad ever get that?"

"Yeah, my grandpa got the book, but I think my uncle has it now," Cam said.

"Is he far away? Do you think he'd lend you the book?" John asked.

"Sure. I'll ask my dad to get the book from him. He lives nearby so it shouldn't be hard to get," Cam said. "I think they were kind of sharing it, anyway."

The three looked over the website a little more. Before long, John and Katie had to leave. Cam walked his friends to the front door. After they left, he went to ask his dad about the book. Cam found out his dad wasn't home.

CHAPTER THIRTY-SIX

The Book

"Well, you're in luck, kiddo. Your dad is visiting with him right now. He went over to show him pictures from your trip," Cam's mom told him. "Give your dad a call on his cell. Ask him to ask Uncle Rob about loaning you the book."

Cam gave his dad a quick call. Later, just before dinner, Cam heard his dad come in. Cam came downstairs to check with his dad. He saw the book sitting on the table.

"Thanks, Dad," Cam yelled, as he picked up the book and brought it back upstairs.

"Wow, that trip did do a lot for Cam," his mom said to his dad. "The trip even got him reading. I'd say money well spent."

"I'll say," Cam's dad said. "He seems to have matured a lot lately. He even cleaned up his room without being asked. And, now this, reading a book, without being asked or made to do so."

Once Cam got into his room with the book, he went to sit down in the chair. He remembered the dog hair just in time. He needed to clean off the chair before he sat in it. He got a lint roller and peeled off the old sticky sheet.

After that, he went to work cleaning his chair. When he finished cleaning, he turned on the lamp and plopped down in the chair. With one foot, he slid a stool over and put up his feet. He was ready.

He studied the cover of the book first. The cover showed the ship after it had turned upside down. Smoke was coming out from the ship and fire was on the water. Most of the ship was underwater. Next, he flipped through the pages. In the back of the book was an index. The index listed all the key facts in the book. Each key fact had page numbers showing where to find them in the book.

Cam looked up his grandpa's name in the index and read those parts next. Cam found the sections the ghost showed up on, too. Cam checked the crew photo. In the photo, all the crew was standing on the deck of the ship. Mike was easy to spot holding Salvo the dog. A page in the book told about Mike working on the oil pipes on the ship.

One page listed men killed when the ship sank. Mike's name was on that list. Then, Cam found pages that cited the author's sources. One source was a woman who gave the stories about Mike. She had a different last name than Mike's. That was some help, but Cam was still annoyed. Nothing said how Mike and Salvo died.

Cam's brief search with the index didn't give him much to go on. He knew he needed to read the book. Reading wasn't a thing Cam liked doing. He wasn't a strong reader. He mostly just read the books he had to for school. But, Cam's interest in this book was not the same. Today he was reading with a purpose. He was looking for answers and he hoped he would find them in the book.

Something clicked in Cam's brain. Cam stopped reading. He looked around his room. He had the feeling Mike was watching him. Nothing happened that he could put his finger on. Nothing was moving or out of place.

Still, things were not the same for Cam. He didn't feel as afraid of Mike as he had before. He couldn't think why. All he knew was that things were different. He picked up the book and started to read again.

The book started when the sub hit the ship. A lot of sailors told their stories of the attack that day. Some men were killed right away. Others lived to tell their stories and those of their friends. Some men had to make their way through the smoke to escape from the ship. Some men went to their battle stations right away. Finally, all the men had to get into the water. They had to swim away from the sinking ship. Ammo and drums of oil were exploding all over the ship.

Some men were lucky. The fire spread on the water after they swam away. Others were not so lucky and had to swim under the flames. Some of those men had to come up for air amid the flames and smoke. The photos showed thick, black smoke above the water. Cam couldn't see how any air would be there for them. The flames grew to over 200-feet in the air.

After the first chapter, the book went back further in time. It talked about some of the crew and how they came to be on that ship. The more he read, the more involved in the story Cam became. Even so, Cam's mind started to wander. He was tired from his long trip. Before he knew it, the book dropped into his lap. He was asleep.

CHAPTER THIRTY-SEVEN

Seems Familiar

Like previous nights, a dream broke up Cam's deep sleep. Cam dreamt he was on the ship. In his dream, the sky was a beautiful blue. The sun was just above the horizon. Cam was standing near the rail of the ship, up on deck. His hands resting on the railing. He was just looking at the other ships nearby. The smell of salt in the air. The ship seemed to sway just a little. Although he could hear the slight sounds of a ship's boilers, the air was calm. He found the sound of the sea very soothing. From behind him, Cam could hear men talking while they worked. Cam felt the warm sun shining down on his face.

Off to the right of the ship, he could see a line of bubbles in the water. The bubbles headed right for him. In his dream, he ran through the hatchway and kept on running. He ran towards the back of the ship. Cam didn't get far before a huge blast rocked the ship. The blast knocked Cam down to the metal deck. Broken glass was all around him. In the dream, Cam started to get to his feet. He stopped when he heard a familiar voice call to him.

"Cam. Cam. Come down for dinner. It's ready." Cam could hear the words but did not understand. *Who's calling me to eat at a time like this? A torpedo just hit the ship! Oh, wait. That's mom's voice.* For an instant, Cam worried about his mom. *Was she on the ship under attack?* As he was waking up, Cam realized he had been dreaming. His dream seemed so real. He looked at the palms of his hands. In his dream, he had cut his hands on some broken glass when he fell. Now his hands were fine. There were no cuts on his hands.

Cam looked up to see his mom in his doorway. She could see what happened. "Oh, you fell asleep. Sorry, but dinner is ready," Cam's mom said to him. She turned and started back down the stairs.

"I'll be down in just a couple of minutes," Cam said. He needed some extra time to fully wake up. His dream felt so real. After his mom left, his room seemed extra quiet. He didn't know why. He had to force himself to get out of his cozy chair.

Cam set his book on the small table next to his chair. With great effort, he stood up. He headed downstairs after a short stretch and yawn. He followed the smell of food.

CHAPTER THIRTY-EIGHT

Is That Dog Old Enough to Drink Beer?

Dinner was ready by the time Cam got to the kitchen. His mom had just put the food on the table.

"Get yourself a glass of milk, Cam. Food's on the table," Cam's mom said as he walked into the room. He still looked a little blurry eyed. Cam's dad was already at the table.

"Wow, I just had a dream I was on Grandpa's ship when it blew up. The dream seemed so real," he told his parents.

"That can happen when you fall asleep reading," his dad said.

"Yeah, I know, but the dream seemed so real. I think I recall hearing a dog barking on the ship, too."

"Well, they did have a small dog as a mascot on board the ship. His name was Salvo. From his pictures, I'd say he was a cute little dog. I don't think you've had a chance to read much of the book yet. The dog used to eat cake and drink beer. Yes, the crew used to give him beer," Cam's dad told the others.

"Do you think that was a good thing for a little dog?" Cam's mother asked. It mattered to her how people treated dogs. She loved dogs but never had one. She was allergic to dogs so the family couldn't have one.

"Oh, I'd say the dog could have some beer. It was good the men took care of the little fellow. I'm sorry he had such a short life."

The three quietly ate their dinner. As they ate, they thought about the little dog. They were thinking about the fact he died when the ship sank. They also felt the small dog must have meant a lot to his owner.

"I wonder what did happen to the dog," Cam said.

"If you want, I can tell you a little or you can read some more," Cam's dad said.

"I think I'll keep reading. It's kind of like reading a mystery book. Cam now looked forward to reading more of the book.

After dinner, Cam went back to his chair and the book. This time, he got further in his reading. His nap in the late afternoon helped him to be more awake now. Three hours flew by. But now, Cam had to stop for the night. He was too tired and his eyes were sore. Reading for such a long time surprised him. That was the longest he'd ever read in one sitting.

He put a bookmark into the book and set it down. Sitting back, he became aware of how quiet the house was. He listened to see if he could hear his parents watching TV. The house was quiet as a tomb. *They must have gone to bed*, he thought to himself.

Cam got up and headed down to the kitchen to get a snack. Halfway down the stairs, Cam recalled he had not had dessert. That didn't happen often.

He must have been right in thinking his parents had gone to bed. Their bedroom door was closed. The lights were off downstairs. He flipped the lights on as he went to the kitchen. Since his run-ins with the ghost, he kept the lights on in the house. Wherever he went he would turn on a light. He didn't want to run into the ghost in the dark.

Cam went straight for the cookie jar. His mom made the best cookies and she baked them often. He opened the lid and stuck his hand inside. He felt let down. The jar was empty except for some crumbs. His second spot to look was in the freezer. There had been ice cream there the other day.

Again, he was let down. All he could find was some frozen yogurt. He and his dad like ice cream, but his mom likes frozen yogurt. She likes the frozen yogurt because it has less fat. *I guess Dad got here before me*, he thought. *I think we need to buy twice as much ice cream as yogurt next time.* The yogurt would have to do. He spooned himself a bowl and put the rest back in the freezer.

Cam headed back upstairs. He was careful not to look back after turning off the lights. He took the last six feet to his doorway in a sort of sprint. He almost lost the spoon from his bowl of frozen yogurt. Happily, the spoon didn't fall. *Ghost or no ghost, I don't want to miss dessert*, he thought.

Once inside his room, he locked his bedroom door. Cam's trip downstairs left him wide awake. He thought to read while he was eating his dessert. He jumped back into his comfy chair. He liked the chair a lot for two reasons. First, the chair was super comfy. Secondly, and maybe the best, the chair let him have his back to the wall. He could face almost all his room and his door. He felt this gave him the best view of anything going on in his room. He no longer liked surprises like he used to.

CHAPTER THIRTY-NINE

No Surprise is the Best Surprise

Cam woke up in the middle of the night. He found himself still in his chair; the book lay open on his chest. The empty bowl sat on the floor near his left foot. The light was still on in the room, of which he was glad. After he put his bookmark in its place, he set the book down on the chair. He grabbed his PJ's from his bed and went to the bathroom. First, he checked the hallway to make sure it was clear. The night light was on and the door was open a crack. Most times he took three steps to get to the bathroom from his room. This night he only took two steps.

The first thing Cam did was to reach in and flip on the bathroom light. He stepped in and locked the door. All the lights in his bathroom were on while he brushed his teeth. Sometimes he would skip brushing his teeth at night. Now, he had to brush to get rid of the yogurt taste left in his mouth.

Cam was sure not to look at the mirror on the cabinet. He knew no one should open their cabinet at night. He was glad he kept his toothbrush in a glass on the counter.

Again, he went across to his bedroom in 2 steps. He felt relieved when he was safely in bed. Of course, he had brought the bathroom nightlight with him to his room. He hadn't used the light for years, but tonight was different. That extra bit of light helped him to fall asleep.

The morning light woke Cam up the next day. *Wow, I slept through the whole night and nothing weird happened. Maybe things are changing for me*, he thought to himself. He hurried to get ready for Katie and John. They were on their way over to be there when he talked with Vera.

Cam had time for a shower. Cam loved long, hot showers. He liked to get lost in his thoughts, surrounded by the steam. He felt the shower helped him forget any problems. He turned on the water and got in when it was hot enough. The hot water on his back soon helped him forget the ghost. He stood there for a long time. He felt great until just after he turned off the water. Still, in the shower, he turned to face the bathroom. What he saw shocked him. There, on the fogged bathroom mirror was some writing. Someone wrote, "Letherknowitwasthedog."

Cam stepped back when he saw the message. *Oh, my gosh. Who wrote that and what do they mean?* He looked around the bathroom to make sure no one was there. Cam knew he had to figure out what the message meant. He didn't wait to dry off. Cam went into his room for his phone. He came back and took a photo of the mirror message. He checked the photo to see how it turned out. A blurry naked figure in the photo startled him. Then he saw he was the one seen in the steamy mirror. He deleted that first photo. The next photo he took was at an angle. This time the image was not a naked selfie. After that, he dressed and hurried downstairs.

Cam was sure glad to see his mom and dad in the kitchen. He wasn't going to tell them what happened yet. He just didn't want to be alone in the house.

Cam's dad was happy to see Cam, too. "Hey, I'm glad you're down early today. I checked my email this morning.

I got one from a reunion group for your grandpa's ship. Seems they liked the photos we took of our dives on the wreck. They invited us to their next event. It's only in about 2 weeks," he told Cam. "By the way, what brings you down so early?"

"I'm going to call Vera this morning. John and Katie are coming over to be on the call with me. Hope you don't mind," Cam said. "That'd be great to go to the reunion. Where is it?"

"That's the great thing, Cam, it's right here in town."

"Cool," Cam said. "So, we'll get to meet Grandpa's friends from the ship?"

"I don't think there are many still alive, but there should be some. Also, a lot of their families will be there. I think there will be kids your own age there, too."

CHAPTER FORTY

It's All About the Dog

A short while later, the doorbell at Cam's house rang. John and Katie had come over. Cam was quick to get the door to let his friends in.

"Hey, Cam," John said, "have any sightings lately?"

"Hi, Cam," Katie said.

"Hi, guys," Cam said. "Yeah, this one was more creepy than scary."

"What's up?" John said as Cam lead them up the stairs to his room.

Cam didn't say anything more until they were all in his room. He didn't want his parents to hear. Cam told his friends about the writing in the bathroom. Then, he showed them the photo he had taken.

"Not quite sure what Mike wants," Katie said. "It's clear it involves the dog. See, he ran the words together, but you can still make it out. 'Let her know it was the dog'. Problem is, who is she? And, what do you need to tell her?"

"I don't know. Maybe he wants me to tell my mom I took the dog tag," Cam guessed. "Kind of looks like he ran out of room on the mirror to write 'dog tag'."

"Yeah, the message is about the dog tag. You weren't

supposed to take it. You did take it from his grave," John said.

"What? Are you kidding?" Katie said. She was a little annoyed. "It's about the dog! The dog! Not the dog tag." She gave the boys a 'what were you thinking' look.

"What about the dog?" John asked. He didn't think it was that clear the message was about the dog. Since Cam had gotten back from his trip, most of their talks had been on the dog tag.

"It must be the dog. What was his name, Salvo?" Katie said. "But, who is 'her' he wants you to tell something to?"

"Maybe it's someone who will be at the ship's reunion," Cam said.

"What ship's reunion are you talking about?"

"Oh, yeah. My dad told me the ship is having a reunion. The reunion will be here in town in just two weeks," Cam said. "He and I are going to go to it. They want to see the photos of the wreck that we took."

"That'll be great. Do you think that's what Mike wanted?" John asked.

"I'm still not sure where the dog comes into this," Katie said. "You did say the dog mostly belonged to Mike. What could he want to tell someone about the dog? They all knew he had the dog."

The three kids felt kind of stumped. They talked about things until it was time to call Vera.

The link was bad and Vera could only talk a short time. A big storm had hit the islands. Everyone was pitching in to clean things up. There was a lot of work to do. Vera had to help. The storm brought down a lot of trees. It even took the roofs off some of the houses. The good news was no one had been hurt. The videocam call didn't last long. Cam was happy John and Katie got to meet Vera. Vera seemed to like them. John was impressed with Vera.

Cam, Katie, and John didn't meet that next week. The mystery of the note on the mirror was just that. It was still a mystery. At the end of the week, they got back together again. In that time, Cam tried to avoid seeing the ghost. He kept busy with the book about his grandpa's ship. It was a slow read, but worth it. The book was the biggest Cam had ever tried reading. By the end of the week, Cam felt like he knew his grandpa much better. The book told the entire story of the short life of the ship and its crew. The author was a son of one of the sailors on the ship. He had thoroughly researched the ship and its crew. Cam couldn't wait to finish the long book.

CHAPTER FORTY-ONE

Fire? Here?

Cam's life had changed. He had never believed in ghosts before. Now, he knows there are ghosts. The note left in the steam still freaked him out. Yet, he was happier to get a note than seeing a ghost. Maybe if he changed his lifestyle, he would not see the ghost.

At night, Cam went through a new night time routine. He would leave a nightlight on in his room and jump right into bed. No longer did he take his time getting into bed. The dreams stopped for a while, but only for a while.

One night, the nightmare came back. In his dream, Cam found himself again on the ship. Again, he heard and felt the blasts and the heat. He felt like he couldn't breathe. Cam woke to find his face into his pillow. *This must be why I felt like I couldn't breathe*, he thought. As he turned his head, he couldn't believe what was going on in his room. There were flames all around his room. He could see thick black smoke lit up by the bursts of yellow and red from the flames. The thought of being in Hell flashed in his mind. Then he noticed the sound of explosions. His room rocked with each wave of force. Cam jumped up to run to the door. He wanted to get to his parents' room so he would be safe. The floor felt hot to his bare feet. He knew his feet were burning, but he knew he couldn't stay in bed. Just getting to the door now seemed very hard. The forces from the blasts pushed him back and he just about fell over. The t-shirt he slept in was sticking to his chest from the sweat.

Cam waved his hands back and forth, trying to fan the smoke so he could see. Once at the door, he grabbed the handle. The hot handle scorched his hand so he yanked his hand back. Pain pulsed through his hand. He thought for a moment and made up his mind. He had no choice so he bravely grabbed the handle. Ignoring the pain, he turned it and opened the door a crack. Cam peeked beyond the door. Flames and black smoke filled the hallway. A huge blast blew the door open the rest of the way. The force of the blast sent Cam flying back through the air. He landed on his back on the floor with a thud. A second thud followed when his head hit the floor. In the next second, he blacked out. He could feel himself waking up slowly. When he opened his eyes, his room was back to normal. The smoke and fire left no signs of ever having been there. His room was as neat as when the ghost cleaned it.

Before Cam could get up, his dad came into the room. The face of his dad looked wide awake. His face contrasted with the "slept in" look of his hair and P.J.'s. "What happened? I heard a big thump and it woke me up. What are you doing on the floor? Are you okay?"

Cam didn't know what to say. His head swung back and forth around the room. There were no signs of the flames and smoke he had just been in. He looked at his palms and feet for signs of burns, but there were none.

Sitting up, he said, "I guess I just had a bad dream. I must have slipped getting out of bed, or something." He rubbed his head with his hand.

"Well, if you're okay, I'm going back to bed. You know if you ever want to talk about things, just let me know." A worried look came over his face. He felt Cam was having too many bad dreams lately.

"I'm okay, really."

"Well, please be careful. You'd better get some more sleep now. 'Night, Son."

"Good night, Dad," Cam replied. Cam's dad pulled the door shut as he returned to his room. Cam froze in place. A puff of dark, thick smoke floated up from behind the door as it closed. Cam got the sense that the smoke had been hiding behind the door. Then the smoke dissolved into the air. Cam thought, *Mike's telling me he's still here.*

CHAPTER FORTY-TWO

Yes, He's Still Here!

Cam gave up on going back to sleep. He stuffed a towel into the crack under his door. Afterwards, he turned on his lamp. Then he sat down in his chair with his feet up. He was wide awake and didn't think he would be able to fall asleep. But, he fell asleep before he knew it.

The sun was bright when Cam woke the next morning. He still wasn't sure if those events truly happened in his room. When he saw his lamp was on, he knew something happened. Then he realized he was sitting in his chair and not in his bed. Cam had a harder time telling what was real or not.

Cam got a few other "signs" during that week. Thankfully, none were as intense as the fire in his room. He got one "mirror message" that read, '*was up to me.*' Another message was, '*Couldn't get him in time.*'

Later in the week, Katie stopped by Cam's house. "Hi, Katie. I'm sure glad to see you. I've been getting more notes from our friend," he told her. "I wanted to get your take on what the notes could mean." The two reviewed the notes.

"I'm sure it's because you took Mike's tag," she said. "That must have made some kind of connection with Mike."

"I've been thinking the same thing," Cam said.

For the rest of the week, Cam racked his brain. He needed to break the link between himself and the ghost. But, how? He thought to just throw the dog tag away, but he could not do that. He had too much respect for the sailors on his grandpa's ship. He couldn't toss out a sailor's dog tag, even if he was a ghost. He was stumped for ideas. He couldn't think of a way to do it.

A new idea came to Cam. He decided to send the tag to Vera. Maybe she or Tony could take the tag to the ship. He wrote a note and put it with the tag in the mail to Vera. Not knowing how much it would cost to mail, he took it to the post office. They told him how many stamps it needed. He paid and they put the letter in their mailbag.

Cam stopped in the doorway of his room when he got back home. There, on his desk, the letter sat. Somehow it came back to him faster than he could get home. *Ghost mail*, he muttered to himself. He knew then that it wouldn't be easy to get rid of the tag.

Cam went back to reading the book for an answer to his problem. He needed to know the whole story. He found the book helped him get to know the sailors better. He focused his reading on Mike and Salvo. He looked for everything he could on the two. He only saw where the book listed them as dead. The book hadn't told how Mike or Salvo died.

In bed that night, Cam's mind was full of concerns and questions. He was worried. He didn't want to see the ghost again. Also, his questions kept going around and around in his head. *What did the ghost want from me? What was the ghost trying to say in the mirror-writings? Why did I find the dog tag; Kai said others had been to the ship before? Just last month another dive group went down to the ship. Will the ghost be at the reunion? Will he always be with me?* Cam finally fell asleep with his thoughts.

CHAPTER FORTY-THREE

Going to the Reunion

Once again, Cam asked his dad, "How long 'til we're there?" Again, he thought he was too old to ask that. *Why do I keep doing that*, he thought?

"It's just an hour away," his father answered him. "I'm glad we can drive and not have to stay at a hotel," he said. "It'll cost a lot less than staying there each night." The reunion was spread out over three days. Sadly, Cam's dad could not get time off from work to go the first day. "At least we'll be able to spend two days at the reunion. I'm looking forward to it." He was glad to go but sorry his own dad wasn't going, too.

It was hard on Cam, missing the first day of the reunion. He didn't want to waste a minute in finding out more about the ship. He thought it would help him get rid of the dog tag.

Like the first day, people were still getting to know each other. The sailors hadn't seen each other in a long time. Cam had no idea there would be so many people there. At least 60 people filled the room. There were 13 sailors from his grandpa's ship. They looked older than Cam had thought they would. Some younger people were there with a sailor who had been on the ship. Some were there who had lost a dad, brother, or uncle when the ship sank. A lot of those people were trying to find out more about their loved ones.

Cam noticed a few kids there his age. Most of the adults there were the age of Cam's dad. Cam stayed near his dad since he didn't know anyone else there. Staying with his dad wasn't so bad. Cam wasn't there to play. He wanted to hear everything he could about the ship. Later, Cam went off on his own to talk to more people. All the people there were very friendly.

One man was taking notes on a clipboard. The man asked the old sailors a lot of questions. Cam went over to his dad when he saw that man talking to him.

"Hey, Cam. This is George. He's here because his uncle was on the ship. He's trying to find out whatever he can for his mom. She wasn't well enough to come to the reunion. She's trying to find out what had happened to her brother. He died when the ship sank," Cam's dad said.

"Yeah, my uncle went down with the ship. Your dad said how you both dove on the ship. How was that?" George asked.

"Diving on the ship was super cool. The ship was so big. Seeing such a large ship down in the water was weird. I guess it was kind of spooky, too." Cam told him how the ship was in two pieces. He also made sure to tell George about the ship's guns. "They were all grown over with plants yet still looked powerful."

George listened to all Cam told him. Cam left out having found and taken the dog tag. He was sorry he took the tag. Cam was not going to tell a soul there about the dog tag.

The three talked for about 20 minutes. Then, they started looking at the photos in the room. Photos of the ship were out on tables. Some of the photos showed the ship before it sank. Cam's dad had brought some of his photos of the sunken ship. Those photos were out on the tables too. Cam was glad they could share their photos.

All day folks asked Cam and his dad about their trip to the ship. Many of them said they would like to visit the ship one day, too. Cam was telling his story one more time when he saw George. George walked up to him.

"Did you ever read the book about the ship?" George asked Cam.

"Yes, I just finished reading the book the other day. I kind of wish I had read it before we went diving on the ship. I think I might have looked at different parts of the ship."

"That must have been cool to go and dive on the wreck. I hope to do that someday. You are quite lucky," George told him. "I'm sure your grandpa would be proud of you."

"I think so too. My grandpa was a great guy. I've always been very proud of him. Now that he's in a book, I'm even prouder," Cam said.

"You are one super lucky young man. You got to meet your grandpa. My uncle died when the ship sunk. I never got to meet him. I was born just after he died," George said.

"Was your uncle mentioned in the book? Which sailor was he?" Cam asked.

"He was Mike Bowers," George said. He was a Seaman First Class. He worked with the pipes on the top of the ship when they moved oil to other ships."

Cam stopped. His eyes got very big. He couldn't say anything for a moment or two. He just stood there and stared. *Mike, his Mike, was George's uncle?* Cam couldn't bring himself to say anything.

George took out a photo from his folder. "Here's the last photo my mom had of him. He's the sailor on the left." George showed the photo to Cam. Cam just stood there and stared at the photo. So many thoughts ran through his head.

CHAPTER FORTY-FOUR

That's Him and His Dog

Two sailors were in the old black and white photo. They were on a street with palm trees in the background. Both sailors were holding a dog. As Cam looked on, goosebumps ran up his arms. At the same time, his shoulders twitched just a little and his head came back. The sailor on the left in the photo was Mike! That would have been startling enough, but there was more! Cam's grandpa was in the photo. And, both sailors held Salvo the dog.

Mike was George's uncle! Cam's grandpa was friends with Mike? Here was a photo of Cam's grandpa. With him were the ghost and the ghost dog. Cam wasn't sure what was happening.

Cam's voice came back to him. "That's . . . that's my grandpa!"

"My uncle was your grandpa?"

"No, the guy with your uncle," Cam said. "That's my grandpa."

"Oh, wow. What are the odds?" George said. He took the photo back to take a better look at it. "My mom said her brother certainly loved dogs. No surprise he was in a picture with a dog."

"You don't know the half of it," Cam said. "We've got to tell my dad." Then, the two of them went looking for Cam's dad.

"There weren't any names on the photo. We never knew who the other man was," George told them. "The Navy sent word in a telegram*. The telegram said his ship sank. They didn't have computers back then. A lot of people didn't even have a phone. They had to send telegrams. Later, they wrote he was dead. That's all they ever told my grandma. They never told them details of the sinking. All these years we've wondered exactly how he died. He was a good swimmer. Plus, he was a good sailor."

Cam and his dad had a lot to talk about on the ride home. The photo was the main thing they talked about. George had said he would get them a copy of it. He said he would bring the copy to the reunion the next day.

At home, Cam made a 3-way phone call. He talked with Katie and John at the same time. He had to talk to them about the reunion. Mainly, he told them about the photo.

"Wow, that's so freaky," John told him. "Especially when you know about the dog tag."

"Yeah," Cam said. "I wanted to tell George about the dog tag. I just couldn't bring myself to do that. I feel almost like I stole his uncle's dog tag."

"I don't think you should think about it like that," Katie said. "First off, you didn't know the tag belonged to Mike when you got it. You said you didn't even know what it was. Secondly, you had not met George yet. You didn't know Mike had any family left."

"I know. None of that makes it any easier to tell George about the tag."

"I guess that photo shows some of the reason why you

got the dog tag. But, we still don't know why Mike wanted you to find it. Also, you still don't know what he wants you to do with it," John said.

Cam scratched his head. "I guess you guys are right."

Once in bed, Cam had a hard time falling asleep. A lot ran through his head. He had no idea his grandpa had been friends with the ghost. Well, he wasn't the ghost back then, he was Mike. But, his grandpa never talked about a guy named Mike. *Why didn't grandpa talk about Mike?* he thought. *Was this one of the things his grandpa said he couldn't talk about?* Cam knew he might never know the answer to that question.

CHAPTER FORTY-FIVE

But Why Did He Give It to You?

That night, Cam was in a deep sleep. In the distance, a ship's bell was ringing. The ringing seemed to get closer the more awake he became. His eyes popped open when he smelled smoke. He sat up, a bit confused. He found he was sitting on the bunk of an old WWII ship. Smoke filled the area of the bunks. The smoke stung Cam's eyes. He could barely see what was going on. Once he could see, he could barely believe what he saw. Sailors were jumping out of their bunks and grabbing life vests. Most of the sailors were running to a hatch. They were crowding to get out. Explosions went off not too far away. He could feel the ship rock with each explosion. Just then, a sailor ran up to Cam. He said, "Have you seen Salvo?"

"You mean the dog?" Cam asked, confused with what he was seeing.

"Yeah, the dog!" the sailor replied. Just then, barking came from outside the room.

Finally, Cam could see the sailor's face clearly. It was Mike! Cam understood. He was aboard the *Mississinewa*. *This has got to be a dream*, he said to himself.

Mike looked back at the men pushing to get out of the

room. He swung his head, searching through the smoke, towards a second hatch. Still more barking from outside that hatch. His attention went to where the men were trying to get out. Their faces filled with panic. Mike's jaw tightened. A determined look came on his face. He took one step towards the closed door. He stopped and turned back to Cam. He said to Cam, "Kid, let my family know what happened to me."

"What do you mean?" Cam asked.

"Tell 'em! Please?" Mike said.

Mike then ran to the closed hatch. He opened the hatch, stepped through it, and then closed it. When the hatch had opened, thick smoke and flames leaped inside the room. The heat hit Cam like a furnace blast.

Just seconds after the hatch closed, a huge blast went off where Mike had gone. The hatch blew open. Again, flames came into the room. This time, the whole doorway filled with flames. The pressure from the blast threw Cam back. Without thinking, he brought his arms up to cover his face.

Quiet filled Cam's ears. Only a second before there was chaos. Now, not a sound. When Cam opened his arms and looked around, he found darkness. Within seconds, his eyes got used to the dark. He could see he was in his own bedroom, on his own bed.

His eyes dashed around his room. He felt he might see the ghost in his room. His room seemed extra quiet and still. The room was nothing like the noise of the blasts and screams he thought he had heard. He had to shake his head to make sure he was awake. *What just happened*, he thought. *Did I just wake up from a dream, or did I travel through time?*

Mike's words, "Tell 'em! Please?" rang in his head. *It all felt so real, the heat, the panic, and the blasts. Was it?*

As he wondered, a twinkle of light came from his night stand. There, lay the dog tag. *How did the tag get there?* he thought. *I left it in a box in my drawer.*

Cam wasn't going back to sleep after that. He picked up the dog tag in his hand and laid back. He saw that even the scarce light in the room made the dog tag sparkle. He happened to look over at the wall near his chair. There, pinned on the wall was his photo of him and his grandpa. Cam was just a tiny kid in the photo. Oh, how he wished he could have been older to talk to his grandpa more. If only he had known to ask about the ship and Mike. As he thought about it, he became a little sad. He realized he wouldn't have known to ask about Mike. He would not have understood what his grandpa went through. He would not have understood how he felt to lose his friends and his ship. A lot more made sense now. Cam could hardly wait for the drive the next day.

CHAPTER FORTY-SIX

We Haven't Heard From Everyone

They left the house early to get to the reunion. Cam had questions to ask his dad. "I was young when I talked with Grandpa. He didn't tell me all that much about his ship. You talked to him a lot about his ship, didn't you? What all did he say about the sinking?"

"I think we've gone over all that before, son," his dad said. "You read the book. I think you know about all there is to the sinking. At least what's known so far."

"I wish I knew more," Cam said.

"Me, too," Cam's dad said. "Who knows, maybe we'll learn more. They have never heard from all the sailors. Maybe they'll find some more who will be able to fill in more of the story. After all, there were other sailors there too. Those sailors who survived the sinking went through a lot. Many of them, like your grandpa, didn't want to talk about it."

"Well, he talked to you about it," Cam said to his dad.

"Yes, he did. He did talk about a lot of things. Some things he kept private. Your grandpa would talk about the ship and the blasts. What he wouldn't talk about much were his friends; those friends who never got off the ship. He kind of blocked those stories out of his head.

He lost so many close friends. He didn't want to think about losing his friends. Just too many bad memories, I guess. For the first two years after the ship sank, he had nightmares. Many times, he yelled out, 'Abandon ship!' in his sleep. Grandma said he often yelled out, 'No, don't go that way!'"

Cam felt sorry to hear his grandpa had bad dreams. *Was he yelling to Mike? Maybe telling Mike not to go out that way?*

Before long, Cam and his dad got to the hotel. They were ready to start the next day of the reunion. Cam hoped to learn a lot more. He hoped George brought the photo of Mike and his grandpa.

"Do you think he'll remember the photo?" Cam said to his dad. He hoped George would keep his promise and get a copy made.

"Yes, I believe he will. At least, I hope so."

Cam and his dad piled out of their car. Next to them was a big, old looking car. The car had a lot of WWII bumper stickers on it. The car was very dirty and not washed in many miles. The license plates showed the car was from Florida. *That car sure came a long way to get here*, thought Cam.

CHAPTER FORTY-SEVEN

It Meant So Much to be There

A middle-aged man with a warm smile got out of the car. He stretched as if he had been driving for a long time. From the far side of the car, an old, white-haired man got out. The older man looked kind of feeble. He was having trouble getting out of the car. The other man helped him and handed him a cane. The older man was thin, except for his large stomach. Cam hadn't seen either of these men before. Cam guessed the driver of the car was the old man's son.

"Hello," Cam's dad said to the old man. "Are you here for the reunion?"

"Yes, I am, sir. Couldn't get here earlier. Our car broke down, but I'm here now!" he said. "This is my son, Tim. I can't drive anymore. They say I can't remember things good enough to drive. I can still drive fine, but they keep saying, "no!" Guess that's what happens when you get old."

"Hi, I'm Cam, and this is my dad, Bill Lund" Cam said. "Were you on my grandpa's ship?"

The old man reached out to shake hands with Cam. "I believe I was. Who was your grandpa?" the old man asked. "Maybe I knew him."

"He was Cameron Lund," Cam's dad said. "He was a Water Tender Second Class. That's who my son is named after."

"Sorry, I don't recall his name. What division was he in? We often used nicknames."

"Gosh, I'm not sure," Cam's dad said. "I'll have to see if I can find that out today and let you know."

"I'd be grateful if you could. We're glad to meet you two gentlemen," the old man said. "I'm Chet Wilson. I was a Machinist Mate on the *Miss*. This is my son, Tim."

"It is an honor to meet you, sir," Cam's dad said, and he meant what he said. Cam's dad enjoyed talking to men who knew his dad. He felt a closer link to his own dad each time he met them.

Cam's dad said to Tim, "It's very nice of you to bring your dad here. I can see he appreciates being here."

"I'm glad to be able to bring him. Being here means so much to him. He's got dementia, so he forgets a lot. His memory kind of comes and goes. At times, it's good and other times he can't recall my name." He slowly shook his head. "He recalls a lot of his Navy days when things are right. I hope we have a good day today."

"Sorry. I do know what you're going through. My dad went through that, too. It's great when they can remember, but so sad when they can't. He'd get so angry with himself when he'd forget things."

Mr. Wilson went straight to the sign-in table. Cam, his dad, and Tim had a hard time keeping up with him. He was excited to start looking for old friends. "We'll see you both later," Cam's dad said to Tim and his dad. Cam and his dad left their new friends at the sign-in table.

Later, Cam ran into George. Cam wasn't sure if he should tell George about his dream. Cam thought it must have just been a strange dream. Surely, there's no such thing as time travel. It all seemed like something out of a movie. Cam couldn't be sure he didn't make up those things in his dream. He had no way to know if those things took place in real life.

"I've got that photo for you, Cam," George said with a smile.

Cam was glad George brought the photo. George pulled out the photo and handed it to Cam. The photo was just like the one George showed Cam the day before. Cam studied the two faces on the photo. He flipped it over. He looked to see if anything was written on the back. The back was blank. Cam gave the photo to his dad. Cam's dad put it in the copy of the book he had brought with him. The book was the one about the ship.

Cam found nothing new about Mike Bowers the rest of the day. The sailors all told their stories. All of them recalled the details of the sinking. They all told thrilling stories. The burning oil and blasts were all around them.

Mr. Wilson sat with other *Miss* sailors he knew. Some told their stories again and again. Tim sat next to his dad: mostly to help him if he needed it.

"Yes, there I was," started one old sailor. "I was still asleep when the first explosion hit. I recall the weather was so hot, I didn't sleep in my bunk. I slept up on the deck instead. The explosion threw me through the air. Landing on that steel deck wasn't fun. I knew more blasts would come so I went right over the side. Swam as fast as I could towards one of the other ships there."

An old, wrinkled faced sailor told his story. "I ran to the Engine Room after the first blast. I worked there until the Captain stuck his head in and said, 'Get off the ship. It's going down.'"

The old sailor went on with his story. "Us guys in the Engine Room took just 3 seconds to head aft. Aft is the back of the ship. The oil covered the water by then. The flames had just moved to where I was going to jump in. I took off my life jacket so I could swim under the flames. I saw some guys who forgot to remove their life jackets. They didn't make it. They died. They couldn't get underwater and floated there where the flames were. I barely came out alive. I came up one time in the middle of the flames and smoke. Tried to get a breath, but all I got was smoke. I had to keep swimming under water. I was just past the flames and smoke when I came up for air. At the time, I didn't think I could make it. Luckily, a small boat picked us up."

"It's amazing what people can do when they have to, isn't it Cam?" Cam's dad said. Cam nodded. He couldn't imagine what those men went through.

"I was in the forward bunk area," Mr. Wilson said. "I remember the flames coming right through there. Most of the guys standing near the door were killed right away. I had a friend, um, his name was . . . uh, gosh, I hate that. I just can't recall names much some days. I can see his face, but it's been too long I guess. Anyway, he didn't make it. Then, I went . . . uh, well, I guess I got off the ship ok. I'm here now." He stopped telling the story. One could see he couldn't recall the details now. He slumped down a little, sad he could not recall all that took place.

His son, Tim, patted his dad on the shoulder. Tim said, "My dad told me that story years ago. He had told his friend not to go forward after the first blast. The friend wouldn't listen to him. Right after the guy went through the door, the second blast went off. That blast killed him."

A few other men added their stories. Most told where they were on the ship when the blasts went off. They also told what they had to do to get off the ship. Cam and his dad sat and listened closely. The stories all involved huge flames and blasts. It was a wonder so many got off the ship alive.

"They will be taking the group photo next. Then, that's about it. I think the reunion will be over," Cam's dad said.

"I'd sure like to come to the next reunion," Cam told his dad. "This one was great. All these old guys and what they went through . . . more people should know this stuff."

"I totally agree. Let's go and watch them take the photo and then we'll have to be on our way."

So, the ship's crew all lined up together for one last photo. Thirteen old men stood tall for the photo. Cam thought about the first crew photo. *That photo was taken in World War II. There were so many men back then. Now just a few and they're all so old.* "Dad, it's sad to see how old they all are now," Cam said to his dad.

"Yes, son, it is. But, we should be glad we got to meet these brave men. The same kind of men who would give their lives for their shipmates. Men like your grandpa. For me, the sad thing is your grandpa couldn't be here with us. But, I know he'd be happy we're here to meet his shipmates."

After the photo, the old sailors stayed in their group. Cam and his dad walked over to them. "It's been an honor and a gift to have met you all," Cam's dad said to the men. "Thank you so much for what you've done. I only wish my dad was with us now." Then, he reached out and shook the hand of each of the sailors. Cam shook each man's hand too. The event moved Cam.

On the drive home, Cam kept talking about the stories he heard. Hearing the stories first hand, he felt like he was on the ship with the men. The whole experience changed Cam. He had much more respect for veterans. He used to just think of them as a bunch of old guys. Now, he remembers they were young guys once. Young guys who put their lives on the line to save the world. "I guess

I'm really lucky to have met those old guys," Cam told his dad. Cam's dad smiled and said, "We both were."

Cam knew when he got home the ghost and dreams would still be waiting for him. But, somehow, he knew he had to go through those to learn more. He knew he needed to learn more about the dog tag and the ghost. He was sure he was ready now for whatever would come.

CHAPTER FORTY-EIGHT

Recalling the Past

Mr. Wilson went back to Florida with his son, Tim. Both men had had a great time. Tim found out more about his dad's time in the Navy he hadn't known. The time Mr. Wilson spent with his old Navy friends had been good for him. Tim saw his dad recall a lot more about his time in the war. Recalling lost friends had made Mr. Wilson sad. But, now his dad couldn't stop talking about the trip. He enjoyed being there so much.

One night, Mr. Wilson was sitting with his son. Tim was going through an old photo album with his dad. Tim knew looking at old photos was good for his dad. It helped him recall his family and the life he lived. Tim played old music his dad liked when he was young.

The old man pointed to a photo. "That's a photo of me the first day I was on the *Miss*," he said. "That one is when we stopped in Hawaii. This other one is a bunch of us outside a bar. We used to drink a lot back then. We just wanted to forget the war. Did I ever tell you, I never thought I'd come back alive? Most of us felt that way."

Tim's whole body shook a little. His dad had never told him that before. He could not think of being in the war thinking he'd never come back. "How'd you do it,

Dad? How'd you get through that?"

"We just did what we were told. Doing what needed to be done. We were fighting for our loved ones."

Tim thought about the burden his dad had put on himself. "You were quite a hero, you know?"

"Hero? Nah. All those other guys who never came home. They were the heroes. The rest of us were just doing our part," Mr. Wilson said. He was thinking about the friends he lost during the war.

Tim heard the same words from his father's shipmates. They all had said the heroes were the guys who never came back home.

Tim's dad pointed to a small photo. Mr. Wilson said, "This fellow . . . he was a funny guy. I recall he found a dog in Hawaii. You know, he brought the dog on the ship. The skipper let him keep it. Said the dog could be the mascot for the ship."

"Dad, that guy! That's the man who Cam and George asked us about. Do you recall that, at the reunion?" Tim said.

"I don't recall them. Guess I forgot. Well, my buddy, Bowers, was a character. He fussed over the little dog. He gave the dog beer to drink. Once he gave the dog some cake to eat," the old man said. Some things were coming back to him. "We all fussed over the little pooch. He was a bit of home."

The music helped the memories come back to the old man. As the old music played, he recalled more about his ship. The memories seem to flood back; the good memories as well as the bad.

"It was so sad. Bowers didn't make it." The old man shook his head slowly. "The dog didn't either," he said abruptly. "One could maybe blame the dog for Bowers' death. I guess we all had to do what we thought best at the time. We could hear the dog barking up forward of the bunk area. Bowers ran out through the hatch to get the dog. He said he needed to save Salvo. That was the dog's name. That was right after the first explosion. I heard another sailor tell him to leave the dog. Bowers insisted he had to save the dog. Walked out through the hatchway. He closed it behind him. Then, the second blast got him," the old man told his son. "The hatch was blown clear off its hinges. When I looked through that hatchway, I could see the deck was torn apart."

At first, the story saddened Tim. Then, a smile came to Tim's face. "That's just what George and Cam were looking for," Tim said. "I'll need to see if I can get a hold of George. I think I have his phone number with all the papers from the reunion."

Tim looked, but he couldn't find anything for George. He must have misplaced it. As luck would have it, he found a contact for Cam's dad.

Faces in the Flames: A Ghost Story

CHAPTER FORTY-NINE

Delivering the News

Each night, for almost a week, Cam had the same nightmare. In it, the sub hit the *Miss* while he was on board. He had just woken up and the sub hit the ship. The blast knocked him down. He was in a bunk area. He could see a lot of guys around him who were not moving. Many of the guys' clothes were on fire. Cam tried to run, but he didn't know what direction to go. In the dream, he found himself in front of a door. When he opened it, a blast would go off and he would wake up from the dream. The dreams drove him crazy since he didn't know how to stop them. The same dream kept playing out in his head each night.

One night while Cam sat in his room, his dad called up to him. "Cam, come look at this! I just got an email from Tim from the ship reunion. He was talking with his dad and his dad remembered Mike Bowers. He told Tim the whole story."

Cam ran down the stairs as fast as he could. Just hearing that news gave him a better feeling in his chest. He felt a great weight lifted from him.

"Tim wrote that he can't find contact info for George. He knows we are looking into the story, too. He's asked us if we could let George know the story."

"Dad, do you think we could tell George in person?" Cam asked. "I remember they don't live too far away. It would sure mean a lot to tell him and his mom at the same time."

"Yes, I'm sure that would be better. I am free tomorrow. We could try to see if they're available for a quick visit. I think a visit to his mom would be nice. She couldn't come to the reunion."

Cam's dad made a quick call to George. He made sure they wouldn't mind a visit. George said that would be fine. He told his mom about the visit. She was eager to have company stop by. This visit would be special to her. She wanted to hear more about her brother's ship.

On the next day, the drive took about an hour. Traffic was very light. Cam and his dad left their house around lunch time. The two had to take an early lunch, but they didn't mind. "It'll be a good time to get there," Cam's dad said. "We don't want to be there at lunch time. It might interfere with their lunch. Also, it would be before she would need to take a nap."

The house was made of red bricks. It looked quite old. The plants looked like they could use some extra care. *Taking care of an old person and their yard must be tough*, Cam thought. At home, Cam always had to do the yard work. He didn't think George had any children to help out.

They didn't have to wait long at the front door before it opened. George answered the door. He looked happy to see them.

"Thanks for stopping by. This means so much to my mom. I told her everything I had heard. She likes to talk to different people. She usually just talks to me all day," George said. "And, there were so many stories last week. I know I didn't recall them all."

"Well, I think we've got a surprise for both of you," Cam's dad said. He couldn't stop the smile from coming to his face. He was anxious to tell George all they had found out. But, he knew telling them might be tough. The news would be about sad things. He hoped they thought any kind of news is better than no news.

George led the two into the living room of the house. Old furniture filled the room. There were old black and white photos on a piano. It made Cam's dad think of his youth. His parent's house looked like this one. George said, "This is my mother's house. I moved in to help take care of her better."

On the wall hung a very old looking photo. The frame it was in was very ornate*. The frame had all kinds of swirled carving. It just looked old. The dark parts of the photo had faded. Also, the white parts of the photo had yellowed from the years. The photo was of two teens next to 3 dogs. They were in front of an old house with a large front porch.

"Hey, that's your uncle, Mike, isn't it?" Cam asked, pointing to the framed photo.

"Yes, and that's my mother with him. They were very young as you can see. It's her favorite photo of the two of them," George said.

In a chair in the room sat an elderly woman. Her hair was completely white. Her many years of life had left her with wrinkled skin. She looked rather frail. Despite looking frail, she had a warm smile and bright eyes.

George said, "Mom, this is Cam and Bill Lund. Bill's dad was a sailor with Uncle Mike. You remember, don't you? I told you how I met them at the reunion," George said. "Do you remember what a surprise it was? There, in the photo, was Bill's dad with Uncle Mike and the dog.

"Cam and Bill, this is my mother, Joyce," George said.

"Yes. That was such a surprise. Thank you both for coming to visit an old lady," she said.

"Our pleasure," Cam's dad said as he put his hand out to shake her hand. "I feel a deep connection. Your brother and my dad served together on the same ship. I'm sorry about the loss of your brother." He held her hand for a moment after shaking it. He wanted to let her know he was respectful of her age. Also, he wanted to show he felt tied to her in some way.

She gave his hand a small squeeze just before letting go. "Thank you. It was so long ago. Mikey's been gone longer than he was with us," she said. "And, it's so nice to find lost family."

"It's our pleasure. And, yes, time does have a way of slipping by," Cam's dad said.

"Sure does," Cam added. Though, right now he felt the time was going by very slowly. He was anxious to jump right in. He wanted to give her their news about her brother. "But, you called him Mikey. I thought his name was just Mike. Was that your nickname for him?"

"Just to my folks and me, he was Mikey. Ever since he was a little boy. We're the only ones who called him that," she said.

Cam and his dad looked back and forth at each other. Cam's dad started to speak when Cam asked, "Can I tell them?"

"Sure," Cam's dad said.

George was wondering what their news was. He could tell the two were anxious to tell it.

"We heard from a man on the ship when your brother was killed," Cam said. "You know, Tim's dad."

"Yes, he was a nice old guy. He couldn't recall much

when I met him," George said.

"Yes, but his son emailed us and we talked to him. He was able to recall a lot more last night." Cam proceeded to tell them what he and his dad had heard. He made sure not to leave anything out of the story.

George's mom just sat there with her hand holding her frail chin. She kept moving her hand to her chin and then to her cheek. Then, back to her chin. She had to let the news sink in. She finally heard how her brother died. It had taken so many years. She was glad she was sitting down. Tears came to her eyes. Her son George gave her some tissues and then sat next to her. He took her hand and gave it a loving little squeeze. They sat there quietly for a minute. It was Cam's dad who broke the silence.

"He was pretty heroic," Mr. Lund said. "He was one who thought more of the lives of others than himself. He wasn't thinking of his own safety. We heard many of the men were new to ships. Those new men got off the ship the fastest. I'm not blaming them. My father never blamed them. He felt they only did what they had to do."

Cam and his dad could see the pride in the faces of both George and his mom. They were so glad they had come to give them the news in person.

"Mikey always loved dogs," Joyce said. "I'm not surprised a bit he went to save that little dog. I recall he was always bringing home stray dogs. Then, he would find nice homes for them."

"Where are our manners, George? Would you please bring our guests something to drink? I'm sure Cam would like some of those cookies we just got."

Cam's eyes lit up. He licked his lips in a show of appreciation. He loved cookies. "That would be great."

"Can I give you a hand?" Cam's dad offered.

"Sure, that would help. It's right in the kitchen, just

this way," George said. "Be right back."

Cam's dad left the living room with George. Cam had to act fast. He knew his dad would be mad at him. He should never have stolen from the ship. He knew Mike's sister should have the dog tag. She would be the person he would want to have it, if anyone.

The young boy reached into his pocket. From it, he pulled out the shiny dog tag and chain. "I need to give you something," he said.

"Oh, you don't have to do that," she replied. "You've already given us so much with this news."

"No, I have to," Cam said. "My grandpa would want me to. Your brother, Mike, would want me to also. My dad and I went diving on the *Miss*. They told us not to take anything. I saw this shiny thing there under the ship. I know I shouldn't have taken the tag, but it seemed to be calling to me. I think I'm starting to understand why I got the tag."

George's mom was watching the young boy. She couldn't guess what he wanted to give her.

Cam held the chain as he extended his arm. The dog tag hung beneath his hand, swaying back and forth. He put the tag into George's mom's hand. Cam could feel it was the right thing to do. He could feel a weight removed from his shoulders. When the tag rested in her hands, Cam let go of the chain. It was done. He knew Mike's ghost wouldn't be visiting him. He didn't know why, but he just knew those visits were over.

Cam kept quiet. He just let George's mom read the dog tag. He saw the broad smile come across her face. Tears rolled down her cheeks. She sat there and sobbed. Cam didn't know what to do. He put his hand on her shoulder and stood there. He wasn't sure how long he stood there. It just seemed like a long time to Cam. He was relieved to hear his dad and George return. The two were talking as they entered the room. George was carrying a tray with some drinks. Cam's dad carried a tray with a large plate of cookies.

"Hey, what happened while we were gone?" George asked. He could see something had gone on while he was away. Cam and Joyce both had serious looks on their faces.

"Dad," Cam said, "I've got to tell you something. When we dove on the wreck, I took something from it."

Cam's dad first looked surprised. Then, he looked a little sad. He didn't want to say anything in front of the others. He would talk to Cam on the ride home.

"Please don't be cross with the boy," Joyce said. "He brought me a present. It's beyond anything I could have hoped for."

"I brought her Mike's dog tag," Cam confessed.

"His dog tag? Really?" George said.

Cam's dad looked a bit amazed. He hadn't expected that.

"Yeah. I got the tag when we were diving. It was shining under the ship. It seemed to call to me and I couldn't help myself," Cam said. "I'm sorry, Dad."

"Don't be sorry on my account," Joyce said. She smiled. "It's just a miracle. I had lost him so long ago. Now I feel like I've gotten him back. I don't know how I can thank you enough." George's mom read the dog tag again. She rubbed her brother's name stamped on the tag. Then, she handed the tag to George so he could see it.

"Wow," George said. "That's just amazing. Tell you what, Mom. We need to make a proper display for it. I can see what awards Uncle Mike got. Here is a photo showing him with awards on his uniform. I know we can get those replaced. I'll put them all together in a shadow box* for you."

"Oh, how wonderful. I'd love that," she replied.

"Super," Cam's dad said. "I've got something like that for my dad's ribbons. Those are well-deserved awards. They won four battle stars. Don't forget to request those, too."

They knew it was time to go back home after they finished the snacks. Cam and his dad reached that point in talking with new friends. All the things that needed to be said had been said. So, they said their goodbyes. They left George and his mom with their thoughts of Mike. The day had been filled with emotion. Everyone was tired. Still, they were tired in a good way.

Cam knew his dad would have something to say in the car. He was dreading that part of the trip. He knew he had done wrong by taking the dog tag from the ship. Still, he helped bring Mike's story to light.

It turned out Cam's dad wasn't too mad. He did talk to Cam about the risks the boy had taken. In fact, he talked all the way home.

Cam had learned a lesson. He gave his word to be more careful. In the end, both Cam and his dad were just glad things worked out so well.

"She sure is a sweet old lady," Cam's dad said.

"Yep," Cam said. "I think Mike will be happy to be home again."

Home again? What did Cam mean by that? his dad thought.

Cam and his dad were rather quiet after they got home. Neither one said much. They both were busy thinking about all they had learned. Both were glad they read the book on the *Mississinewa*. They also thought about the men they had met. A lot had gone on at the reunion. Everyone had been happy to be there. Still, an undertone was clearly felt. Those at the reunion knew that this reunion one would most likely be their last. The men who served in WWII were very old. Most had already died. Those men left were getting frailer, or forgetful, or both. Most who came had to have help getting there.

As Cam pondered this, a thought came to him. He realized Mike Bowers had him find the dog tag. Cam thought he knew the reason. Mike must have known there will be no more reunions. This reunion was his last chance to get his story out. He wanted to get his story known. When Cam came along, that was Mike's chance. Cam was the best person to give the dog tag. After all, he was the grandson of an old friend and shipmate.

Cam felt better about all the things that took place. He felt better about taking the dog tag. Now, he knew it was meant for him to take the tag home. He went to his dad.

"Dad," Cam said. "I've been thinking. I think I was right bringing that dog tag home. How else would it have gotten back to Mike's sister?"

"You may be right, this time, Cam. I've been thinking about the very same thing. Seems like Mike wanted to make sure his family knew how he died. If we were in their place, we would want to know. I'll bet Mike is resting happily now."

Later, Cam called Katie and John. He wanted to talk about what had taken place. They had been waiting for his call. They both came over to his house right away.

Cam told them all about the visit. He told them Joyce and George were happy to get the tag. "I can't lie, though. I'm sure glad to not have it anymore. And, my dad didn't get mad I took the dog tag. I kind of thought he would freak out."

"That was good he was cool about it," John said. "Maybe you can tell me your secret and I can use it on my dad."

"Not much of a secret. Just get something from a ghost. Give it back to his family. Simple," Cam said and smiled. "But, visits from a ghost sure are creepy. I'm glad he was a friend of my grandpa."

"You sure were lucky there," Katie said. As Cam told the story, Katie felt strange. She wasn't sure why. "Do either of you feel something odd right now?" Katie asked.

"No," both boys answered. "Strange in what way?" John asked.

"I'm not quite sure what it is. I'm not sure if I feel Mike being here or him not being here," she said. "I'm pretty sure he's gone, though."

"Me, too," Cam said.

CHAPTER FIFTY

Farewell, Mike

There were no more sightings of Mike after that.

Some months later Cam heard some news. Cam's dad got an email from George. He handed the email to Cam to read. In the email, George wrote his mom had passed away. She had died in her sleep. He said her death was from old age. He also wrote, "She could let things go now that she knew how Mike died." She was at peace. George thanked both Cam and his dad. "You have no idea how much that meant to my mom. It meant a lot to me, too. She always thought he would have died helping others. Uncle Mike had promised he would come back when the war was over. Thank you, for helping him keep that promise," he wrote.

Cam was sad to hear George's mom died. "Remember, Cam. You brought so much joy and closure to her. She didn't have any of that. You gave a lot when you told her Mike's story and gave her his tag."

"I guess so," Cam said, nodding slowly. Cam thought about all the men killed in wars. How many loved ones never learned how they died? He sat down and wrote an email. He sent it to the author of the book about his grandpa's ship. Cam wanted to make sure the author knew how Mike died. Maybe he could add Mike's story to the website. That way, Mike's story would be out there for the world to know.

Cam talked with Vera and Tony on a video cam from time to time. Not as often as they first thought. They talked about every two or three weeks. They all were busy with school and life in general. Vera was glad to hear Cam gave the dog tag away. She was a little afraid of it. She was happy the tag found its rightful home. "Mike's sister and nephew should have the dog tag. Lea was right. She kept telling me Mike's spirit was in the tag. Lea said Mike put his trust in Cam. He wanted Cam to tell his story. That's because Cam was the grandson of a friend. I guess she was right."

"Are you going to let Lea know she was right? I wouldn't," Tony said. "She's hard to live with now."

Cam had to laugh. "I'll leave that between you three," he said. Cam said his goodbyes and ended the call.

Then, Cam opened a scrapbook he had made. It had photos and things from his grandpa's days in the Navy. Cam picked up the photo of Mike and his grandpa. He just stared at the photo for a minute. He saw the cute look of a happy puppy on Salvo's face. Cam could see how innocent the dog looked. The dog's safety was in Mike's hands. There, in the photo, was something he saw for the first time. When he took a good look, Cam saw a look in Mike's eyes. He saw Mike's head tilted a little. Also, Mike's right eye was almost closed. Mike had looked right into the lens when they took the photo. Cam seemed to think Mike had winked at the camera. *Who was the wink meant for? Cam maybe?* He wondered. An odd thought jumped into his head. Cam turned the photo over to see its back side. The back side of the photo used to be blank. Now, he saw some words scribbled on the back. It read, '*Goodbye and thanks. Your grandpa would be proud. Thanks, kid! (signed) Mikey.*'

THE END

Q&A FROM THE AUTHOR

Q1. Was there really a USS *Mississinewa*?

A1. Yes. The U.S. Navy had a ship called the USS *Mississinewa* (AO-59). The ship was also known as the *Miss*. The *Miss* was put in the water in March, 1944 during World War II. Like the ship in the story, the *Miss* sank. It sank on November 20, 1944. A suicide submarine hit the *Miss*. Sixty-three men died due to the sinking. A huge fire started. The fire went around the entire ship and burned oil on top of the water.

Q2. Do you have a link to the *Mississinewa*?

A2. My father was a sailor on the *Miss* when she sank. He went to his battle station when the ship was struck. He worked there for about 15-minutes. He was the one who actually thought his mother would be told he was dead.

Q3. Were there really faces in the photo of the ship burning?

A3. Yes. I could see what looked to me like 18 faces in the smoke in the real photo.

Q4. Were the people in the story real?

A4. The people in the story were not real, kind of. Some of the things in the book were like things that did take place on the real ship. There really was a dog named

Salvo. Salvo did drink beer and eat cake. Sadly, he died when the ship sank. One sailor mostly owned Salvo. His real name was Joseph De Santis. He also died when the ship sank. Also, another sailor, John Maher, died when he tried to save Salvo. Smitty was the nickname of the Chief Water Tender, Edmund Smith. He did die after he left the fire room. Other than Smitty and Salvo, the names were made up by me.

Q5. Can people SCUBA dive on the *Miss* today?

A5. Yes. The ship is in 130 feet of water at Ulithi Atoll. People go there to dive on the wreck. They can't go into the wreck. Going inside is not safe. Also, the ship is a war grave. Dozens of men were killed inside the ship and their bodies were never recovered.

Visitors to the ship stay at the Ulithi Adventure Lodge. Ulithi is in the middle of the Pacific Ocean. I have never been there and have only seen their hotel online.

Q6. Were there any real paranormal events linked to the *Mississinewa*?

A6. Per *Miss* families, two events took place. The 4-year old child of a *Miss* sailor woke from a nap yelling, "Daddy's in the water!" The child woke at the same time her dad was in the water at Ulithi. She was in New York. Also, one wife of a *Miss* sailor woke up after having surgery crying, "He's (her husband) dead!" A week later, she received word that he had died when his ship sank.

DISCUSSION QUESTIONS

1. What are some of the reasons why people find it important to know more about their ancestors (family members who have lived and died)?

2. When Cam first arrived at Ulithi, do you think he was correct in that all the islanders were staring at him? Have you ever felt out of place in a new environment? What did you do about it?

3. Cam didn't follow all the rules while diving on his grandfather's ship. Do you think he should have, or did he have a good reason not to? When is it okay not to follow the rules?

4. How did Cam's opinion of the old sailors change as he heard more of their stories at the reunion? Are your first impressions about other people often right?

5. Even though Cam, Vera, and Tony have social media to communicate, why is it difficult for them to keep up their friendship?

GLOSSARY*

SCUBA: short for **S**elf **C**ontained **U**nderwater **B**reathing **A**pparatus, i.e., tank of air and other equipment to allow someone to swim underwater for an extended period of time without coming up for air.

WWII: Short for World War Two. War fought around the world. The United States was involved from 1941 to 1945.

Blotches: Red spots on the skin

Swells: Up and down movement on the surface of the water caused by the tides

Constant: Non-stop

Lush: Plants that are very green and wet

Desperate: Having an urgent need or desire

Neoprene: an oil-resistant synthetic rubber

Queasy: Inclined to or feel nauseous, i.e., ready to throw-up

Amazed: Overwhelmed with surprise or sudden wonder

Cramp: The uncontrollable tightening up of a muscle

Urge: An involuntary, natural, or instinctive impulse

Keepsake: Something that reminds the owner of an event or place

Current: Movement in the water caused by the tides. Also, can mean up-to-date.

Antiseptic: Germ killing liquid or gel

Tetanus: An infection that results in tightening of muscles (lungs) that can be fatal

Trio: Three of something

Panicking: Losing control of one's mental state; not being able to think straight

Flattered: To receive excessive praise or compliments

Fatal: Able to cause death

Vivid: Strikingly bright or intense

Telegram: means of sending a message over wires, before the use of email

Ornate: Fancy or very intricate

Shadow Box: A deep picture frame to display items thicker than a photograph or painting

FACES IN THE FLAMES

THE TRUE STORY

BY R. FULLEMAN

BOOK
TWO

GENERAL TIME LINE

1850's
   Japan opens for trade with other countries

December 7, 1941
   Japan attacks U.S. Navy at Pearl Harbor, Hawaii

December 8, 1941
   U.S. declares war with the Empire of Japan

December 11, 1941
   Germany and Italy declare war on U.S.

May 18, 1944
   USS *Mississinewa* put into service

November 20, 1944
   USS *Mississinewa* sunk by Kaiten

May 8, 1945
   War in Europe Ends

September 2, 1945
   War with Japan Ends

Have you heard of terrorists' attacks in the world? It's awful! People killing others by blowing themselves up?! Suicide bombers! Do you think suicide bombers are a new thing? If you do, then you'd be wrong.

A suicide bomber sank the ship my dad was on in World War 2. My dad, Ray Fulleman, told me about it. I've also talked to other sailors from that ship. This book tells what some sailors went through to escape their burning ship as it sank.

ESCAPE AND SURVIVAL: THE SINKING OF A U.S. NAVY SHIP IN WORLD WAR TWO

A sailor in Japan's navy ran his small sub into a U.S. ship. He did it early in the morning. The date was November 20, 1944. The small sub carried one man and over a ton of explosives. It was near the end of the war. Japan was losing the war. They felt they had to do something extreme. The Japanese thought to use suicide subs. With this sub, it would only cost the life of one man to sink a U.S. ship. It was this first time they used suicide subs that they sank my dad's ship.

U.S.S. *Mississinewa* (AO-59)

1. Boiler (Fire) and Engine Rooms
2. Aft (rear) Crew Bunk Areas
3. Aft (rear) Well Deck
4. Forward Crew Bunk Areas
5. Area Hit by Kaiten
6. Airplane Gas Storage Tanks

A QUICK LOOK AT HOW THE WAR STARTED

The nation of Japan kept to itself for thousands of years. Things changed for them in the 1850's when they opened their country to the world. Japan started trading goods with other nations. People of Japan liked what they saw of other countries. They wanted to be more modern like those nations. Soon, they wanted to become a world power. There was a problem though. To be a true world power, they needed to keep growing. But, their small land did not have enough natural resources.

As trade grew, so had the military in Japan. Japan thought to use their army. They took what they needed from nearby nations. Nazi Germany was doing the same thing in Europe. Japan thought it might work for them, too.

Japan had one big worry about doing this. They worried that the United States would try to stop them. The U.S. had a powerful navy at that time. The United States Navy was a big threat. Japan needed to destroy the U.S. Navy for their plan to work.

To do this, Japan came up with a plan for a secret attack. Japan sent ships loaded with airplanes to attack the U.S. Navy. Most of the U.S. Navy was in Hawaii at that time.

The attack took place on December 7, 1941. They struck the ships and airplanes at Hawaii. Most of the attack took place at Pearl Harbor. The attack was a surprise. It came early on a Sunday morning. Japan sent 366 planes to bomb the Navy. (1) Japan had not declared war against the U.S. before the attack.

Japanese pilots killed 2,330 Americans in the attack. They sank many U.S. ships and destroyed 188 airplanes. Because of that attack, the U.S. declared war on Japan.

That was the start of World War Two (WWII) for the U.S.

It took a while for the U.S. to build its navy back up. During that time, the Japanese were winning the war. Luckily, the U.S. had a lot of resources. They used them to make thousands of new ships. They needed them. Fighting in both the Pacific and Atlantic Oceans took a huge number of ships and men.

In 1943, my dad, Ray Fulleman, was 20 years old. He joined the navy. The first ship he served on was the USS *Mobile*. The *Mobile* was a type of combat ship. He was on that ship for about one year. After staying awake during one long battle, he fell asleep with his arm hanging over the edge of his bunk. Because he was so tired, he didn't move at all while he slept. When he woke up, he couldn't move his arm. The metal edge of his bunk pinched a nerve

The Navy moved him from the *Mobile* due to the problem with his arm. After a long stay in the hospital, he could use his arm again. The Navy then assigned him to the ship, USS *Mississinewa*. (Pronounced MISS-IS-SIN-E-WA) *Mississinewa* is hard for people to say. Most people just call it the *Miss*.

The *Miss* was an oiler. An oiler is ship that brings fuel oil and gas to other ships. It's like a floating gas station. But, instead of a ship going to the gas station, the gas station goes to the ship.

Combat ships only ran about a week before they need more fuel. They ran on fuel called, "bunker C oil." Planes on aircraft carriers ran on gasoline. The oilers brought the needed fuels to the fighting ships. The *Miss* held about 100,000 gallons of gas. The *Miss* also held millions of gallons of bunker C oil. You can see how it made it easier for the fighting ships. Those ships only had to go a short way from the fighting to get more fuel. Then they could quickly get right back into the fight.

KAITEN COMING

Kaiten Model I

By 1943, some of Japan's leaders did not think they could win the war. The Japanese were afraid of the U.S. raiding their country. They thought the Americans would be very brutal. The Japanese looked to new ways to improve the outcome of the war.

Two Japanese Navy officers devised a plan to help win the war. Sub. Lt. Sekio Nishina and Lt. Hiroshi Kuroki invented a new weapon. They called the weapon *kaiten*. *Kaiten* means "Heaven Shaker" in English. They thought it might 'shake things up' and change the direction of the war. The *kaiten* was a suicide submarine. The sub was made from a torpedo. The torpedo would hold 2,000 pounds of TNT. TNT is a powerful bomb.

In those days, most torpedoes were shot from submarines. They aimed the torpedo at the target and it would go in a straight line. At times, a target would move and the torpedo would miss. A torpedo could not be used when things were in front of the target. Torpedoes could only go in a straight line. There had to be a direct route for the torpedo to the target.

With a *kaiten*, a man could control where the torpedo went. He could steer it at a moving ship. He could also go around other things to hit the target ship. Of course, they had to get men who would give their lives to save their families and country. They were able to find young, single men who were willing to do just that. The problem was, could the men control the *kaiten*.

Steering a *kaiten* was not easy. *Kaiten* did not have computers in them. The pilots opened or closed valves to control their depth. They also had to use a stopwatch and map to figure out the course. He had to do all this on his way to killing himself. *Kaiten* pilots needed to be well trained.

At last, on November 8, 1944, the first *kaiten* left Japan for their secret mission. A farewell party was held for the crews of the 3 mother subs. Each mother sub carried 4 *kaiten* on her deck. In total, twelve *kaiten* left for the first mission. Subs I-36 and I-47 would strike at Ulithi Atoll. I-37 would strike at Palau Island group. (2)

Kaiten co-inventor Nishina was one of the twelve pilots. He brought the ashes of his friend, Kuroki, with him on his mission. A training accident earlier took the life of *kaiten* co-inventor, Lt. Kuroki.

Sub Lt. Sekio Nishina (L) who piloted the suicidal *kaiten* attack at Ulithi. Lt. Yoshinori Kamibeppu (R), planned to pilot a *kaiten* from I-37. He died when the mother craft I-37 sank in the diversionary attack at Palau. Photo courtesy of *Kaiten* Museum.

The main site for the secret mission was Ulithi Atoll. The U.S. Navy had over 200 ships there. Lots of targets for the *kaiten*.

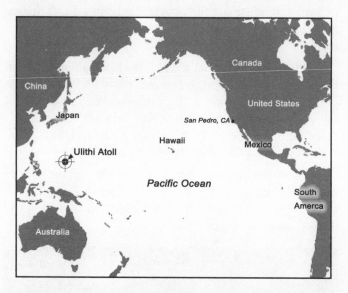

Still, it wouldn't be easy for the *kaiten*. Atolls are hard to get into. There were only a few ways into it. The main entrance had a net across it. This kept most of the enemy ships out.

The atoll was a good place for the U.S. ships. The water was shallow. That made it easy for the ships to anchor. The water outside the atoll was too deep to anchor in. Also, the entrance with the net made it easier to guard.

Atoll: A group of islands, or reefs, that grew up around a volcanic island. After the volcanic island erodes, the surrounding reefs remain and create a barrier to the shallower waters where the volcanic island once was. Atolls take millions of years to be created. (3)

On November 19th, the sub, I-37, got to Palau Islands. Palau was the second target for the secret mission. When I-37 surfaced, U.S. ships saw her. Two U.S. ships hunted the sub for almost 8-hours. They kept listening underwater for sounds from the sub. They dropped depth charges when they finally found the sub. An extra-large under water blast rocked the ships. A huge air bubble broke through the water's surface. It seemed to be the largest the captain had ever seen. The bubble was 25-feet wide and about 5-feet high. It was not like any other sub sinking before. (4)

I-36 and I-47 waited just north of Ulithi. The *kaiten* pilots spent the day playing cards and chess. That night they were given a special meal. They had ice cream for dessert. Some of the men were surprised how easy going the *kaiten* pilots were. The officers of I-36 and I-47 did not like using suicide weapons. Their goal was to have everyone come back safely from each mission. Now, for a mission to be a success, someone from the sub had to die.

Three out of the eight *kaiten* had problems when it came time to launch. The two subs were only able to launch five *kaiten*. The first *kaiten* to be launched was Nishina's. The last words heard over the phone system from the last pilot to be launched were, "Tenno heika banzai." This means, may the Emperor reign for 10 thousand years. It was still dark outside at that time. Also, it would have been very cold inside the *kaiten*.

The inside of the *kaiten* was very cramped. It was a tight fit for the *kaiten* pilots. A small seat and many valves filled the cabin area. The rest of the sub was full of explosives and the propulsion gear. The propulsion system is what made the sub move.

Nishina made his way to just inside of the atoll. There, he saw a large number of ships. A few of the U.S. ships saw Nishina's sub as it lined up to hit its target. The ships sent out warnings of a submarine in the atoll.

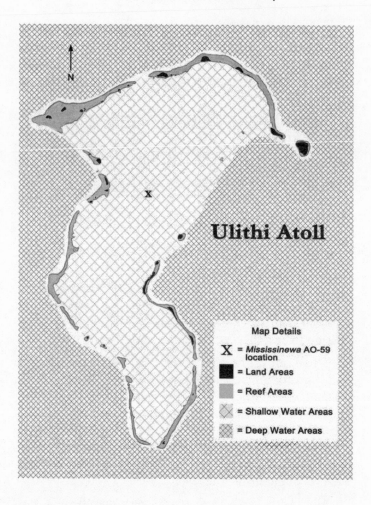

WHY DID NISHINA PICK THE *MISSISSINEWA?*

No one knows why he chose to hit the *Miss*. There are a few likely reasons. It may have been because the *Miss* was a large ship. It was 553 feet long. At water level, the Miss might have looked like a bigger combat ship. Another reason is that he saw the *Miss* was nearly full. It was sitting low in the water and was an easy target. Lastly, it could be that by sinking an oiler its fuel is kept from other ships.

The time was 5:45 in the morning. The crew had just been woken up about 15 minutes earlier. They would start their morning work schedule at 6:00 a.m. Many of the men were getting ready for work. Some of the men tried to get extra sleep. They liked to sleep as long as possible.

Nishina's sub hitting the right side of the *Miss* made a huge blast. The ship rocked to the left and back to the right. The blast threw several men to the deck from where they were sleeping.

THIS WAS THE FIRST SHIP FOR MOST OF THE CREW

In 1944, most men put on a ship had not worked on a ship before. The *Miss* was no different. Only about 40 percent of the crew had served on a ship. For the other 60 percent, the *Miss* was their first ship. Even some of the officers were new to ships.

In many cases, how much time men had spent on ships played a part in whether they lived or died. Many untried men went into the water after the first blast.

Within moments a second blast rocked the ship. A gasoline storage tank next to where the sub hit the *Miss* was empty except for fumes. The gas fumes lit and caused a huge blast. Still more men jumped into the water after the second blast.

THE SAILORS' STORIES...

Ray Fulleman, WT2c - Went to his battle station

Some men didn't go over the side right away. Ray Fulleman was in the aft port bunk area when the sub first hit. Grabbing onto his bunk was all that kept him on his feet. He went to the nearest outside door to see what had happened. Through the hatch he could see the sky was bright red. The second blast went off and he ran to his battle station. The boiler room was his battle station. It was only a few feet away from his bunk. [Note: Sailors go to their battle stations during any combat. They are supposed to work there. Fulleman worked on the boilers in the fire room. He fed the water used by the boilers. Boilers make steam. Steam is what made the propellers turn. The propellers made the ship move in the water.]

Two other sailors were there in the boiler room. Fulleman started to light a boiler. His boss, Chief Smith, got there right after Fulleman. While the four worked to get all boilers lit, they heard many smaller blasts. Chief Smith told one of the men to see what was happening up on deck.

Fulleman went up one level in the fire room. From there, he controlled the water going into all the boilers. A few minutes later, a man stuck his head in the fire room doorway. He had been in the engine room.

"Get off the ship! It's going down," he yelled to Fulleman. "The Captain just gave the word to abandon ship."

Fulleman yelled to the men in the fire room below. He told them they all had to get out. The men shut down all the boilers except one. They left that one up in case it was needed. It was about 15-minutes since the first blast. The men all tried to get out of the fire room through a hatch on the right side. Heavy, thick, black smoke came in when they opened the hatch.

They quickly slammed the hatch shut. They turned and went up one level within the fire room. There, they tried a hatch on the left side of the fire room. It opened into a hallway that was only starting to fill with smoke.

Chief Smith asked the two men if they'd seen the man sent topside before. At that point they had lost track of that sailor. They were not sure if he had ever returned. "Fulleman, go make sure he got out of the fire room!" Then, the two sailors started down the hallway to the rear of the ship.

Fulleman looked into the fire room from the hallway. He called the man's name a couple times, but with no answer! He knew the man would be dead if he had still been in the fire room. Thick black smoke was now coming out of the fire room.

As this was happening, Fulleman heard a man yell, "You can't go aft! The ammo is blowing up there."

Fulleman thought to himself, "Oh, Jesus. My mom's going to get a telegram (It would mean that her son was dead). Just as he said that, he saw a guy run through the smoke forward in the hallway. He thought if that guy could make it, maybe he could too. So, he went that way. It led him to the lowest deck on the ship. The deck was just about 4 or 5 feet above the water.

He looked out and saw that the wind was holding the flames back. There was an open 'V" shape free from flames in front of him. He let himself down into the water. He then swam through the thick Bunker C oil floating on the water. The Bunker C oil was about 10 inches deep. With each stroke he swam, he saw his hand sink into the thick, gooey oil.

Fulleman swam just past the thick oil to a waiting boat. Sailors in the boat pulled him into it. In the boat were the sailors from the fire room. Only Chief Smith wasn't there. Smith was never seen again. (Fulleman found out how Smith died 65-years later. One of the many oil drums blowing up had landed on Smith. It killed him instantly.)

Lieutenant John Bierley – Ship's Doctor

The ship's doctor, John Bierley, was in his cabin when the sub hit. He shared the space with one other officer. That man was Herbert Allen. Both men were asleep in their bunks when the first blast hit. It shook the ship back and forth violently. Both men woke up instantly. Doctor Bierley stood up right away. He turned to reach for his uniform pants. As he turned, hot flames shot through the open portholes.

Luckily, he was not facing the flames. The flames burned the back of his hands and head. He gave up on the idea of getting dressed.

Both men knew they had to get out of the cabin and

off the ship. The two quickly stepped into the hallway.

The blast from the main storage tank sent new flames through the hallway. Bierley raised his arms to cover his face. By doing this, his shirt rose up on his back. The exposed skin burned at once.

The men started walking in the hallway. The flames and smoke made walking difficult. Doctor Bierley had nothing on his feet. He stepped on something hot and hurt his foot.

A third officer came into the hallway from his cabin. He saw that Dr. Bierley did not have a life jacket. He asked the doctor where it was. Dr. Bierley told the man it was 'back in sick bay'. Sick bay is where the doctor normally worked on the ship. So, the officer gave the doctor his life jacket.

The three men ran down to the next lower deck. That deck is called the Boat Deck. From there, Dr. Bierley saw that the oil had spread to the left side of the ship. Luckily, the flames were 20 feet away. They had not yet come along the side of the ship. He jumped over the side and into the water.

The salt water stung his burned skin. He swam away from the ship and the flames. He just got to a safe distance when someone in a small boat called out to him. Feeling safer, he turned back to see Allen and Wilson. The two officers were trying to escape the flames behind them.

He was shocked to see a new wave of flames overtake the two men. He did not see them swim out of the flames. The fire killed the two men.

Men in a small boat pulled Bierley to safety. The small boat took him to the hospital ship, *Samaritan*. On the *Samaritan*, he got medical treatment for his burns. He wanted to use his medical knowledge to help the doctors on the ship, but they wouldn't let him. He had to just be a patient instead of a doctor for a while.

Raleigh A. Peppers, ST3c – Ship's Steward

Raleigh worked on the *Miss* as a steward. He was the highest-ranking steward on the ship. In 1944, the Navy was like the rest of the United States. The military kept all parts of the Armed Services segregated. Non-combat jobs were the only ones open to black sailors. They lived in their own areas, away from the white sailors. On the *Miss*, their bunks were next to the main forward bunk area. As a steward, Raleigh planned meals. Also, he served the officers their meals. He took care of their laundry, as well.

When the *Miss* was hit, Raleigh was the first to leave the black steward's bunk area. He ran to the nearby stairs to get out of the forward bunk area. When he got there, he briefly froze from fear and could not go up. The rush of men trying to get up the stairs to safety pushed him aside. He worried his friend might not know to get out of the bunk area and off the ship. He tried running back, but too many men were running up the stairs. Finally, he went up the stairs himself. He got to the port side of the ship and jumped into the water. He swam away from the *Miss* and a nearby rescue boat picked him up.

John "Jack" Mair -
A 19-year old farm boy from Wisconsin

Jack Mair was still in High School when Japan struck at Pearl Harbor in 1941. He lived on a farm in the state of Wisconsin. Jack joined in the Navy after finishing High School. Like most of the crew, the *Miss* was the first ship for young Mair. Mair did well in his training. He gained the rank of Fireman Second Class. (Firemen ran the gear in the engine and boiler rooms.) He worked mostly in the engine room. He also did various tasks with the crew.

Mair slept under the cargo deck when allowed. It was a cooler place to sleep than his bunk. He was sleeping there when the *kaiten* hit the *Miss*.

The blast knocked him to the deck. He felt the blast might have been the result of an accident. Drops of hot oil fell on him as he rushed to his locker inside. He went to get his pants and shoes. Fire engulfed the entire bow of the ship at that time. From a quick look, he saw the water off the entire right side of the ship was on fire. The left side was only on fire halfway back. He couldn't find his life jacket. He feared he might not swim well enough to get away from the flames.

Men crowded the ship's back-port side. They waited for their turn to jump into the water. When it came for his turn, Mair jumped the 20 feet to the water below. From there, he swam to one of the rescue boats in the water. Sailors in the boat pulled the boy to safety. The small boat picked up all the men who could fit, then left the area.

**Fernando Cuevas, S2c -
Older than most on the *Miss***

Fernando Cuevas was born in Puerto Rico. Later, he moved to the United States with his father. He was 33 years old when the Navy drafted him. As the war went on, the need for more men grew. Older men were drafted to fill that need. Cuevas' wife was pregnant at the time. He was able to wait until after the baby was born to go into the Navy. Cuevas left his wife and new son early in 1944 to start his basic training. The Navy assigned him to the *Miss* after that. There, he worked as a cook since he had been a short-order cook before the war. So, at 34 years old, he was one of the oldest sailors on the *Miss*.

The morning the *Miss* was hit, Cuevas was at work in

the ship's kitchen. He quickly ran to the crews' quarters before he left the ship. He wanted to make sure they were awake. A nearby boat later picked up Cuevas. The boat took him and others to the ship, *Pamanset*.

**Frank Wilcox, S2c – Tried to save Moran,
but was not able to help**

Frank Wilcox, S2c, went to the back of the ship, away from the most flames. There, he found Peter Moran, S1c, frozen with fear. Moran held onto the railing and would not let go. Wilcox tried to pry Moran's hands off the railing. Peter Moran yelled that he could not swim. The frightened sailor was too scared to let go. Wilcox tried to talk him into letting go. Some of Moran's friends were in the water. They called for him to jump in too. Wilcox told Moran that they would jump in the water at the same time. But, Moran didn't jump when Wilcox did.

After men pulled Wilcox into a boat, he looked back for Moran. No one could see Moran at the rail anymore. No one would ever see Moran again.

Salvo – Ship's Mascot
Joseph De Santis, S2c

Like many of the ships during the war, the *Miss* had a dog on board. The dog was named Salvo. It was picked up in Hawaii when the ship stopped there. The sailor who found Salvo was Joseph De Santis, S2c. The young sailor got permission to keep the dog on the ship.

The dog reminded many of the sailors of their lives back home. He was very popular with the crew. The young men would feed him cake when it was available. They also fed him beer.

Salvo was forward of the bridge when the *kaiten* hit the ship. The crew believed the second big blast killed Salvo.

**John "Jack" Maher, Jr., SK1c –
Lost his life trying to save Salvo**

Jack Maher was a well-liked 22-year old. He worked as a store keeper on the *Miss*. Like many of the crew, he had a fondness for Salvo, the ship's dog.

Maher was in his bunk when the *kaiten* hit. His bunk was in the forward bunk area. It took him only seconds to decide to make sure Salvo was safe. Maher hurried to the forward hatch. That was the direction where the blast came from.

A friend took hold of Maher's arm. "Where are you going? We've got to go the other way!" he said.

"I've got to find Salvo," Maher told him. "I've got to get the dog." He shook himself free from his friend's grip and went forward through the hatch. A large gas storage tank below deck blew up just after Maher got there. That blast was large enough to kill anyone forward of the bridge. No one saw Maher after that.

Maher's wife of 2 years, Patty, was only 23 years old. The Navy sent her a telegram. It said her husband was Missing in Action. A week later, the Navy said Jack was presumed dead.

**Commander Philip Beck -
Captain of the USS *Mississinewa***

The first blast woke Captain Beck. The second blast threw him out of his bunk. He hit the wall and ended up on the floor. Looking up, he saw flames come through the open portholes. The flames looked like welding torches to him. He was glad to be on the floor, away from the flames.

He crawled out of his cabin and into the hallway. It was very hot. A man was lying in the hallway. The man was unconscious or dead. Beck dragged the man out onto the deck. From there, he got the man down to the boat deck.

On the boat deck, Beck saw two sailors running to the back of the ship. He ordered them to put a life jacket on the unconscious man. He wanted them to throw the man off the ship. That way, the man might have a chance to survive.

As he looked around, he saw everything that could burn was on fire. He couldn't see anyone else there. He ran to the officers' cabins. He shouted to get off the ship.

After trying to warn the officers, he went to the rear of the ship. The ship had a steam smothering system to help fight fires. Sadly, he couldn't get to the valve to open it. There was too much fire and steam at the valve. He couldn't get to it.

Beck made his way to the back-right side crew's bunk area. There, he found a life jacket and put it on. He continued his efforts to get the men off the sinking ship.

Seeing the huge flames to the right of the ship, he went to the left side. Small blasts were going off the entire time. Ammo and oil drums were exploding all around the ship. He found two officers and two sailors there on the left side of the ship. The men used fire extinguishers to cool off the deck. With the deck cool enough, they made their way to the back-left edge of the ship. Two of the men used a rope ladder to get into the water. The other three jumped into the water.

A small boat from a nearby ship picked the men out of the water. Captain Beck and two others were the last men to get off the sinking ship.

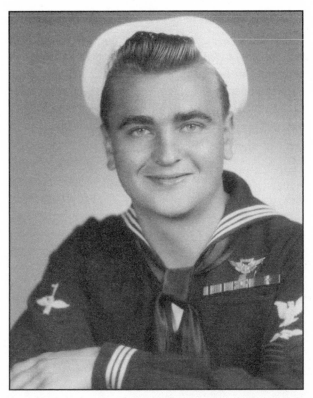

Russell Evinrude, RM2c - Floatplane Radioman

Hundreds of ships sat at anchor in Ulithi that day. A few of those ships carried airplanes on them. The Cruiser *Santa Fe* carried a float plane on board. The float plane launched off the ship. Later, the plane landed on the water to return back to the ship.

The morning of the attack, the float plane from the *Santa Fe* was in the air. The pilot, Blase Zamucen, saw the ship on fire. He also saw the men in the water. He knew they needed help.

So, he landed his plane near the burning oil. He turned his plane. The propeller blew some of the flames away from the men.

The float plane carried two people. One man was the pilot. The other man in the plane was Russell Evinrude. He was the radioman in the back seat.

As part of their rescue efforts, Evinrude got out of the plane. He slid along to the back of the plane. From there he threw out a rope to men in the water. Then, the plane pulled the men away from the flames.

Three months later, the two men were given medals for what they did. They received the Navy and Marine Corp Medal of Heroism. By their actions, they had saved about 20 men.

Kingfisher Float Plane similar to one used by
Zamucen and Evinrude

**Simon "Sid" Harris - Sailor aboard fleet tug, USS
Munsee (and his photos)**

Sid Harris wasn't on the crew of the *Miss*. He served
on the fleet tug, *Munsee*. The *Munsee* was about 2-miles
away when the *Miss* was hit. Several fleet tug boats were
in the area that morning. The tug boats had pumps and
hoses to fight fires on other ships. The tugs could pump
sea water through their hoses.

Sid Harris shared his battle station. That morning, the
other sailor got there first. Sid didn't have a specific job
to do. So, Sid asked if he could take photos of the ship
fighting the fire. His skipper said yes.

The fire was all around the *Miss* by the time the

Munsee got to it. Other tugs came to fight the fire too. Right away, all the tugs started spraying the burning ship with water. It was a dangerous job. Ammo on the *Miss* started to go off from the heat of the fire. That meant the bullets were firing and flying through the air.

To best fight the fire, the *Munsee* came up to the right side of the *Miss*. While they sprayed water from the *Munsee*, men went aboard the *Miss*. The men had fire hoses to fight the fire while on the *Miss*. When the sea water got up to the men's thighs, they knew the ship was going to sink. The men left the *Miss* and jumped back into their tug boats. Shortly after that, the *Miss* turned over to port (to the left). Then, the front or bow of the *Miss* sank down to the ocean floor. Air trapped in the back of the ship kept it floating for one more hour. Finally, all of the *Miss* sank down on the ocean floor.

PHOTOS OF THE ACTUAL SINKING
AND
FIREFIGHTING EFFORTS

Fire completely surrounding the USS *Mississinewa* AO-59. Fleet tug boats start to battle the fire. Small rescue boats from nearby ships can also be seen in the photo.

USS *Munsee* crew spraying water on cargo deck of
USS *Mississinewa*. (Photo by Simon "Sid" Harris)

USS *Munsee* crew spraying water on rear deck of USS
Mississinewa where ammunition blew up.
(Photo by Simon "Sid" Harris)

USS Munsee crew spraying water amid ship of
USS Mississinewa. (Photo by Simon "Sid" Harris)

USS *Munsee* crew spraying water near the bridge of USS *Mississinewa*. (Photo by Simon "Sid" Harris)

USS *Munsee* crew watching as USS *Mississinewa* turns and sinks. (Photo by Simon "Sid" Harris)

THOSE HURT OR KILLED

Rescue boats took the survivors to nearby ships. The USS *Samaritan* moved within the atoll to be near the *Miss*. The *Samaritan* was a big hospital ship. It had doctors, nurses, and most of the gear of a hospital. The rescuers took the severe burn victims there first. Doctors and nurses helped those hurt the worst. Medics and doctors on other nearby ships took care of the little burns and cuts.

Doctors could only name a small number of the dead. Many bodies were burned too badly to see who they were

The Navy first buried the dead on nearby Asor Island. As soon as they could, they moved the bodies to Guam Island. Shortly after that, the Navy moved the bodies again. They sent the bodies of known sailors to their families. The rest were buried in Hawaii.

USS *Samaritan* (AH-10) Photo Courtesy of National Archives #80-G-314193

USS *Solace* (AH-5) Photo Courtesy of National
Archives #80-G-425616

THE LUCKY ONES

From their time in the water, the *Miss* crew were all covered in thick bunker C oil. The rescuers needed to wash the thick oil off the men. To do this, they had the sailors stand in tubs of diesel oil. The rescuers wiped them with the diesel oil. In the next tub, rescuers cleaned the men with gasoline. The gasoline took off the rest of the oil. Each tub of oil or gas helped clean the men more and more. At last, they could shower or see a doctor.

On many of the ships, men collected extra clothes for the *Miss* crew. Later, boats moved all the *Miss* crewmen to the ship *Wichita*. The *Wichita* was too damaged to fight any more. It would sail back to the United States in a few days.

It took two weeks for the *Miss* sailors to return to the States. The *Wichita* sailed into San Pedro, California, on December 15, 1944.

USS *Wichita* (CA-45) Photo Courtesy of Naval Historical Foundation #NH 90428

When the crew got to the dock, they had to wait on the ship. Few men had uniforms. Most only had work clothes. All the other sailors left first. The Navy didn't want the public to know about the sinking. Officers ordered the sailors not to talk about it. After much waiting, trucks came. They took the crew to barracks on the navy base. A few days later, they got new uniforms. After that, they were given 30-days Survivor Leave. They could go home for a visit. Most men lived on the East Coast. They had to take trains to get home. Some stopped at the homes of friends who died in the sinking. Those men told the families what took place.

After a 30-day leave, the crew came back to San Pedro. Most got new jobs on navy bases. Those men did not go back to sea. The Navy sent only a few men to new ships and back to the war.

THE UNLUCKY ONES

The Navy had to let the families know who died. Doctors could only name a small number of the dead. Many bodies were burned too badly to see who they were. Those men had to be listed as "Missing in Action".

During that war, the Navy told little to the families of those who died. Many got two telegrams. The first came about 2 weeks before Christmas. It said their loved one was missing in action. The second came a week later. It said the sailor was still missing and the family should presume him dead. The telegrams only told the dates of death. Telegrams never told how or where the men died.

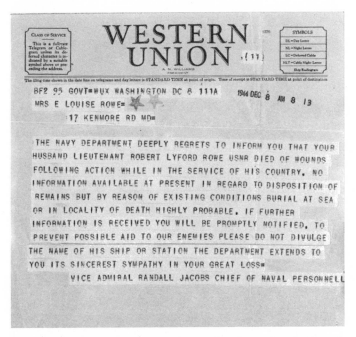

Telegram sent to Mrs. Rowe, letting her know her husband died of his wounds following "action" while in the service of his country. No mention of his ship, location, or what type of wounds.

RESULTS OF THE ATTACK

- 126 *Miss* sailors wounded
- 63 *Miss* sailors dead
  - 45 Missing In Action (MIA), body never recovered, or presumed dead
  - 18 identified dead
- 118 Japanese sailors dead **

  (** Includes the crew of I-36 sunk at Palau the day before the strike at Ulithi, and the *kaiten* pilots.)

I-36 and I-47 left Ulithi. They went on to fight until the end of the war.

The war with Japan ended ten months after the *Miss* sank. The date was September 2, 1945. It was only in the 1950's when Japan and the U.S. became allies. (5)

USS Mississinewa Crew Photo

USS *Mississinewa* Reunion, 1999
Corpus Christi, Texas – 1999 (Seated L-R), John Bayak, Ed
Kinsler, Larry Glaser, Fred Schaufus, Andrew Johnson, Winston Whitten, Harold Ritchie, Bill Gimmeson, Al Bell, John
Mair, John D'Anna, Fernando Cuevas, James Lewis, (Back
Row L-R) Robert Jones, Earl Givens, Ray Fulleman, Earl Van
Orden, Jim Cunningham, Gus Liveakos, James "J.P." Hammond, Fred Caplinger (Photo courtesy of Mike Mair, Ron
Fulleman, Sarah Bright, reunion co-hosts)

FINDING HISTORY

My dad first told me about the *Miss* in the 1960's. Only in 1998 did I start to study the *Miss*. That was the year I met Mike Mair. Mike's dad was also on the *Miss*. Mike never heard about the *Miss* from his dad. His dad never talked about the ship. Like many other sailors whose first ship was the *Miss*, the sinking was just too horrific to talk about. I found Mike Mair on the internet. Mike was looking for sailors from the *Miss*. He wanted to write a book about the ship for his dad. Mike collected information from the Navy about the ship. I was able to find a lot of the crew through the internet. I also worked with the Veteran's Administration. They gave me the status of each man.

There have been three *Mississinewa* reunions. *Miss* sailor Bill Dennehy put together the first reunion. That was in Dorchester, MA in 1989. Eleven *Miss* sailors went. (Even at that time, those at the reunion did not know a *kaiten* sank their ship. They all thought it was two-man subs firing torpedoes.)

Only at the second and third reunions did the crew find out about *kaiten*. The second reunion took place in 1999. Twenty-three *Miss* sailors went to it in Corpus Christi, TX. The third reunion was held in Seekonk, MA. Thirteen *Miss* sailors went to the 2003 reunion.

From the last two reunions came two books. Roughly 60 crewmen and officers were interviewed. (5)

SOURCES

(1) "Pearl Harbor." Gale Encyclopedia of U.S. History: War, Gale, 2009. Global Issues in Context, go.galegroup.com/ps/i.do?p=G-PS&sw=w&u=vale41196&v=2.1&id=-GALE%7CEJ3048500170&it=r&asid=d1c-586359cb73e11d77101df0e725be0. Accessed 24 Oct. 2017.

(2) Mair, Michael. *Kaiten*. Vol. 1. New York, NY:Penguin Group US, 2015.

(3) "Corals." *NOAA National Ocean Service Education: Corals*, 21 Mar. 2018, oceanservice.noaa.gov/education/kits/corals/coral04

(4) www.combinedfleet.com/I-37.htm (lost w/crew of 113) -1January2018

(5) Allinson, Gary D. "Japan." *World Book Student*, World Book, 2018, www.worldbookonline.com/student/article?id=ar285600. Accessed 27 Feb. 2018

(6) Mair, Michael. *Oil, Fire, and Fate: The Sinking of the USS Mississinewa (AO-59) in WWII by Japan's Secret Weapon*. SMJ Pub., 2008.

(7) The official site for USS Mississinewa (AO-59) www.ussmississinewa.com

ABOUT THE AUTHOR

In 1998, while searching the internet for his father's ship, the *Mississinewa*, he came across the son of another *Mississinewa* sailor who was starting to research the ship. Fulleman offered to help and eventually initiated contact with over a third of the crew through internet searches and an improved website. The fruition of these efforts allowed for two *Mississinewa* ship reunions, a primary source reference book of the ship's events, and closure for many of the families after finding out what happened to their lost loved ones. Fulleman continues to host the ship's website and Facebook account in an effort to continue to bring his father's ship's story to the public and descendants of those who served aboard her. Additionally, Fulleman focuses on collecting and labeling the ship's crew on his website by obtaining crewmen's photographs.

During these last two decades, the author has also written, and self-published 3-Hi/Lo books for middle school students. His stories are written at lower reading levels to assist beginning readers at gaining proficiency. He wrote "Faces in the Flames" to encourage young readers with an interesting story while giving them an opportunity to learn why honoring the memory of those who sacrificed so much in WWII is important.

R. Fulleman is a native of Southern California and presently resides there with his wife Lorraine